CONTROL CIRCUITS
By Tom Henry

MW00575079

Copyright © 1992 by Tom Henry. All rights reserved. No part of this publication may be reproduced in any form or by any means: electronic, mechanical, photocopying, audio/video recording or otherwise, without prior written permission of the copyright holder.

National Electrical Code® and NEC® are Registered Trademarks of the National Fire Protection Association, Inc., Quincy, MA.

While every precaution has been taken in the preparation of this book, the author and publisher assumes no responsibility for errors or omissions. Neither is any liability assumed from the use of the information contained herein.

This book was written as a study-aid for an electrician preparing to take an electrical examination.

As you read this study-aid book you will note that complicated electrical circuits and explanations have been put in a clear, concise, understandable language for the *electrician..*

"Written for an electrician by an electrician".

Tom Henry

ISBN 0 - 945495 - 27 - 7

Preface

The information presented in this book has been prepared as a basic manual on controls for the electrician.

Control is a broad term that means anything from a light switch to a complex system with relays, timers, etc.

In my teaching of Code classes to prepare an electrician for an examination, I find many electricians that are not familar with control circuits and have never worked on any. This becomes a big disadvantage on an electrical examination when control questions are asked.

This book contains the actual language used in the exam questions. Personally, I don't always agree with the way the question is asked or sometimes the incorrect symbols that are used on the drawings.

Keep in mind as you answer the exam questions asked, you are looking for the **most correct** answer to each question.

Tom Henry

TABLE OF CONTENTS

Let's start at the beginning, in theory we learned to have a complete circuit we need a source of supply, wire and a load.

The ceiling light in your home is **controlled** by a switch. This is called the basic two-wire circuit.

As the circuit is shown to the right, this would be called a main wiring diagram. These diagrams are converted in **schematic** (ladder) diagrams. The schematic diagram provides a short cut for troubleshooting a control circuit. The schematic diagram includes **symbols** as well as words and phrases. The symbols are interconnected by lines to show the flow of current through the devices.

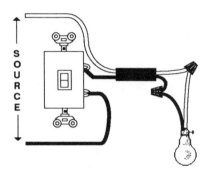

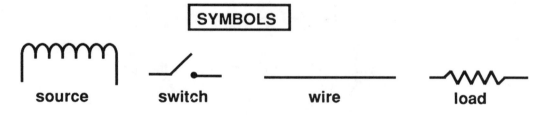

Using the symbols we will put the same two-wire light circuit into a schematic diagram.

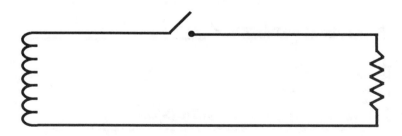

With the switch open there is not a complete path for current to flow back to the source, this is called an **open circuit**.

open circuit

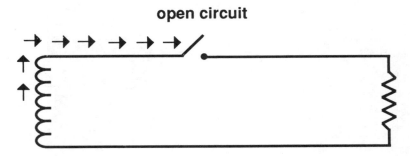

Once the switch is closed there is a complete path for the current to flow back to the source, this is called a **complete circuit**. The switch is the **control** for the circuit.

complete circuit

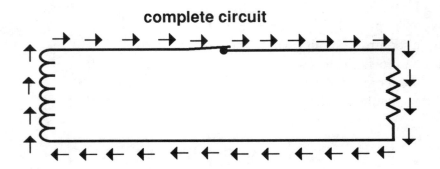

With the circuit **open** there would be **voltage** from the source to the open switch and from the source to one side of the load as shown below.

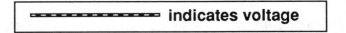

indicates voltage

open circuit

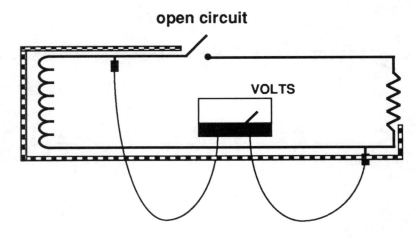

VOLTS

From the source to the **open** side of the switch there are zero volts.

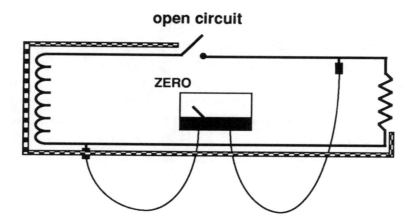

The **load** must have a source voltage applied to both sides to complete the circuit and allow the current to flow.

Shown below is a wiring diagram of a light connected through two 3-way switches. The light can be turned on or off from either switch.

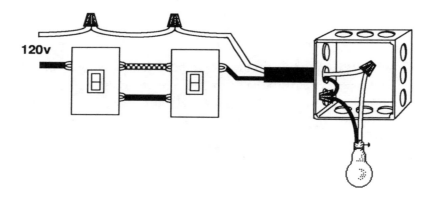

This same 3-way switch circuit is shown below in **schematic** form.

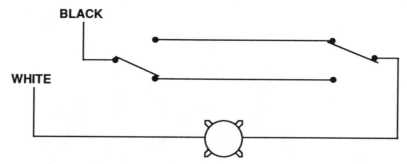

One wire is connected from the source directly to the load. The other wire is connected through the switches to control the load.

It is easier to understand how the 3-way switches can control the light if you see how the switch is built internally. Shown below is a side view of how the 3-way switch is contructed. The black wire is connected to terminal screw **1**. The view to the left shows when the toggle is turned to the "up" position there is a **complete** circuit through terminal screws **1** and **2** and an **open** circuit between **1** and **3**. The view to the right shows that when the toggle on the same 3-way switch is turned to the "down" position there is a **complete** circuit through terminal screws **1** and **3** and an **open** circuit between **1** and **2**.

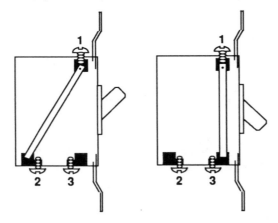

The load would **not** be energized in the circuit shown below. One wire is connected directly from the source to the load. The other wire from the source is controlled through the two 3-way switches. There is voltage from the source through terminal screw **1** and **2** on switch #1. The voltage continues through the wire and stops at terminal screw **2** on switch #2. There is an **open** circuit between terminal **2** and terminal **1** on switch #2.

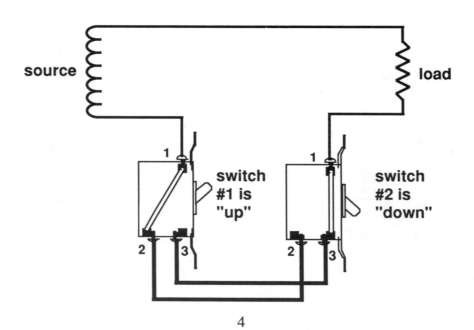

4

When switching switch **#1** from "up" to the "**down**" position the load now becomes **energized** as there is a complete circuit through terminal screws **1** and **3** on switch #1 and through terminals screws **3** and **1** on switch #2 and on to the load. By switching **either** switch #1 or switch #2 the load can be turned off.

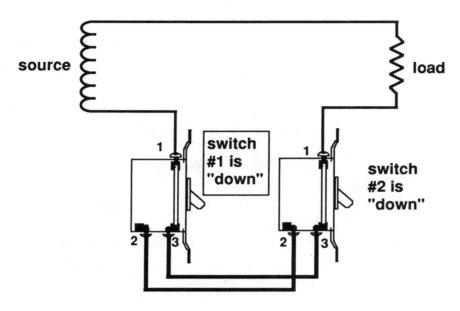

Turning both switches #1 and #2 to the "up" position will also **energize** the load as shown below. And by turning either switch the load can be shut off. It is very important for the student, at this point, to be able to trace a **complete** circuit from the source to the load through the action of the switches, terminals and wiring before advancing to the more complex motor control circuits.

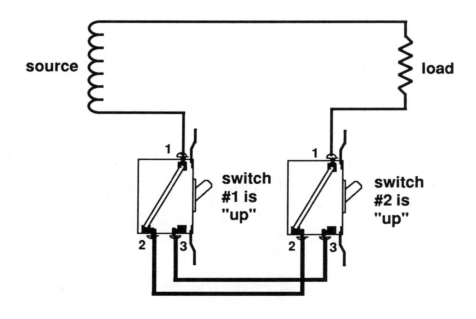

5

4-WAY SWITCH

When a load is required to be switched from more than two switching points a 4-way switch must be used in the circuit. 3-way switches are connected to the source and to the load with the 4-way switches connected in between.

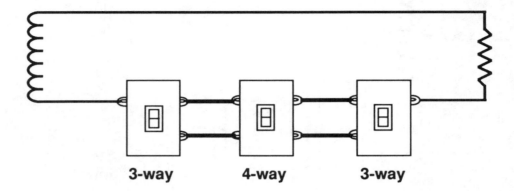

3-way　　　　**4-way**　　　　**3-way**

Don't confuse a 4-way switch with a double-pole switch. A double-pole switch will have "on" and "off" marked on the toggle. A 4-way switch has **no** "on" or "off" markings and is constructed so that the switching contacts can alternate their positions as shown below.

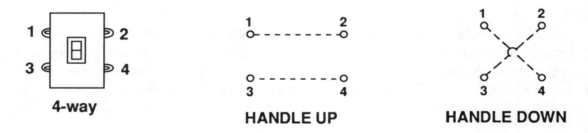

4-way　　　　　　**HANDLE UP**　　　　**HANDLE DOWN**

There are many different types of **switches** used in control wiring. It is important for the student to be able to trace the circuit through these different switches.

One of the first control switches was a knife switch, used to control the starting and stopping of motors.

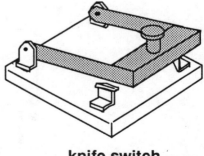

knife switch

6

SELECTOR SWITCH

one normally open

2 position

LEFT

1 o o 2

RIGHT

1 o o 2

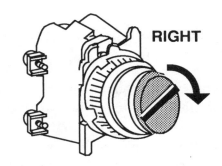

RIGHT

one normally open - one normally closed

2 position

LEFT

1 o o 2
3 o o 4

RIGHT

1 o o 2
3 o o 4

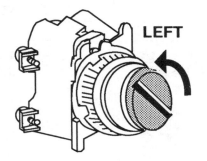

LEFT

one normally open - one normally closed

3 position

LEFT

1 o o 2
o o
3 o o 4

CENTER

1 o o 2
o o
3 o o 4

RIGHT

1 o o 2
o o
3 o o 4

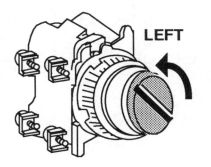

LEFT

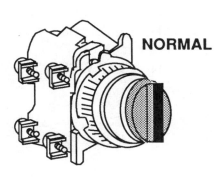

NORMAL

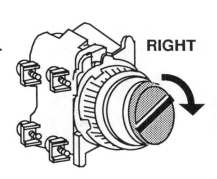

RIGHT

7

LIMIT SWITCH

A limit switch is used in a control circuit to start, stop, forward, reverse, etc. some operation of a machine.

A limit switch generally has two contacts, one normally open and one normally closed quick make, quick break, snap action type.

It is very important when reading a schematic diagram that contains limit switches that you are familar with the symbols for limit switches.

Shown below are the symbols for limit switches. Note the position of a normally open contact in the **normal** position and then in a position with the arm moved to the right or left. Now the normally open contact is **held** closed by some mechanical function in the sequence of the machine operation.

LIMIT SWITCH SYMBOLS

Normal position of the arm 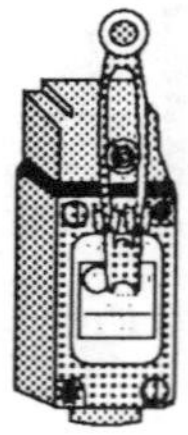	Normally open contact 	Normally closed contact 

Arm position to the right 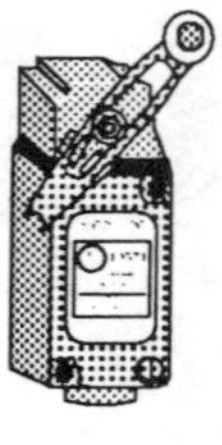	Normally open contact HELD CLOSED 	Normally closed contact HELD OPEN 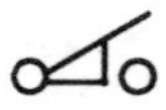

Arm position to the left 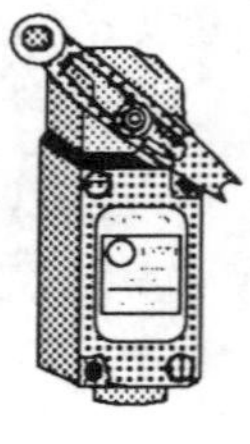	Normally open contact HELD CLOSED 	Normally closed contact HELD OPEN 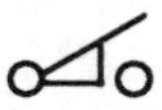

8

PRESSURE SWITCH

normally open

normally open - HELD closed

normally closed

normally closed - HELD open

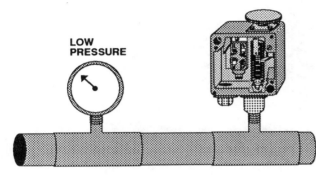

LOW PRESSURE

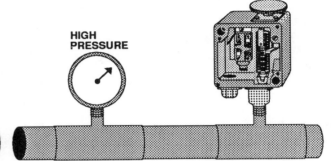

HIGH PRESSURE

FLOAT SWITCH

normally open

normally open - HELD closed

normally closed

normally closed - HELD open

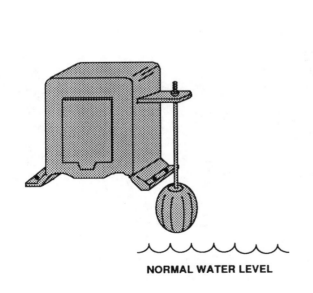

NORMAL WATER LEVEL

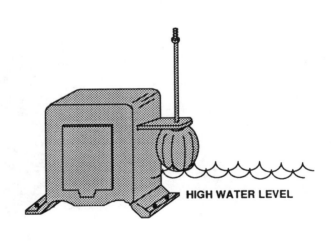

HIGH WATER LEVEL

FOOT SWITCH

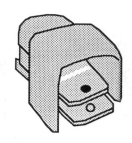

normally open   **normally closed**

FLOW SWITCH

normally open   **normally closed**

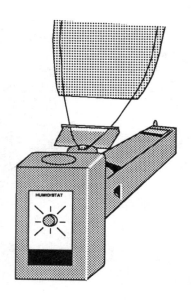

HUMIDISTAT

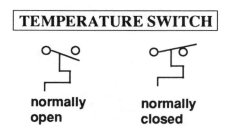

TEMPERATURE SWITCH

normally open   **normally closed**

A temperature switch is a control device that responds to temperature changes. A bi-metallic strip is used to actuate the electrical contacts. The bi-metallic strip is made of two pieces of different metal laminated together. Metals when heated, will expand and contract at different rates. Heating the bi-metallic strip will cause it to warp or curve which will open the normally closed contacts.

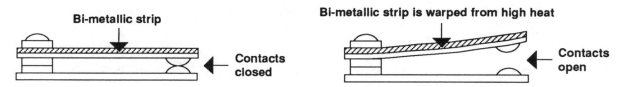

Once the tripping action has taken place, the bi-metallic strip will cool and the warped shape will go back to the normal shape, closing the contacts. A circuit breaker uses the bi-metallic action only the circuit breaker will need to be manually reset to close the contacts.

A gas furnace and a clothes dryer are examples of equipment that uses the bi-metallic action for safety precautions when high heat arises. A gas furnace has a high heat bonnet which will open the contacts to the main gas valve shutting off the gas so the furnace will not be exposed to high heat damage. An electric clothes dryer also utilizes a high heat safety, opening the power contacts to the heating elements when a dangerous high heat is reached.

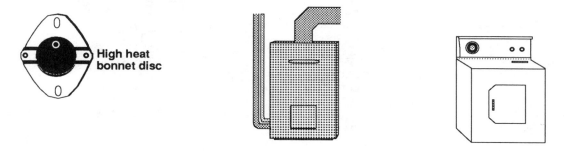

A thermostat uses a **spiraled** bi-metallic strip which increases temperature range and sensitivity.

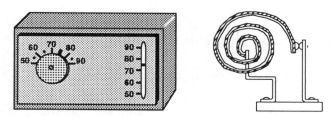

11

RELAYS

Relays, solenoids, etc. contain a magnetic coil when energized by an electrical current passing through it causes the iron armature to move in the frame.

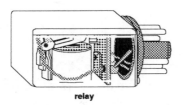

relay

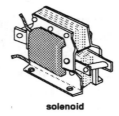

solenoid

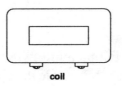

coil

Relays are used in industrial assembly lines, machine tool control and commercial equipment. Relays are **switching devices**. A relay is used in a control circuit as a switch. Relays are not designed to carry large currents.

The 4-pole relay shown has four normally open contacts. The contacts are referred to as poles.

When the coil is **energized** creating a magnetic field it will draw the iron plunger "up" closing the normally open contacts. This is the switching action of a relay. The 4-pole relay contains four switches which can be normally open or normally closed.

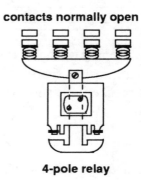

contacts normally open

4-pole relay

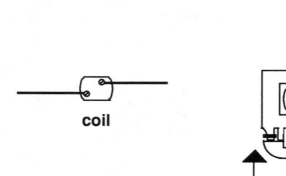

coil

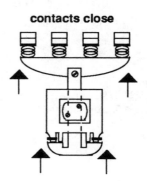

contacts close

On the schematic the coil will have a symbol. ◯
coil

The relay will be given a designation such as R1. (R1)
coil

The four **normally open** contacts will be shown on the schematic as: $\dashv\vdash_{\text{NO}}$ (R1)

If the relay had normally closed contacts the symbol on the schematic would be: $\dashv\!\!/\!\vdash_{\text{NC}}$ (R1)

12

If the relay designation is R22, the relay coil and relay contacts would also be designated R22. Any contacts physically attached to the frame of R22 would be marked R22 on the schematic. Schematics are shown in the de-engergized (power off) position. When R22 is energized the normally open contact becomes closed and the normally closed contact becomes open.

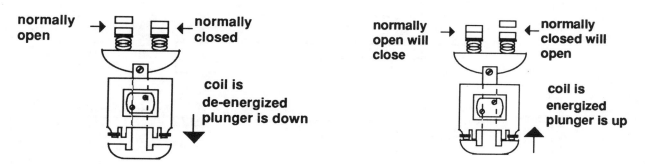

Shown below is a 2-pole relay with one normally open contact and one normally closed contact in a circuit with a limit switch with a normally open contact and two lights. The industrial control circuit requires the "**green**" light to be lit in a **normal** condition. When the limit switch is "**closed**" the "red" light is to be lit and the "green" light is to be off.

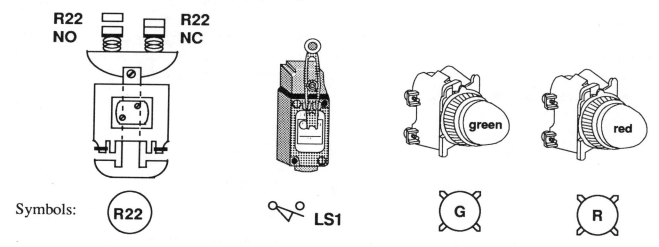

Symbols:

The source will be shown on the schematic as "L1" (line one) and "L2" (line two).

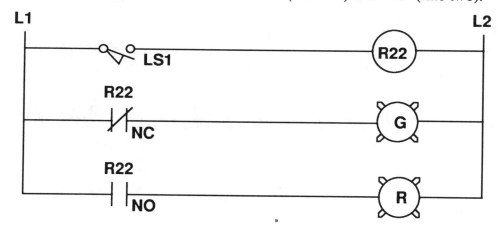

13

Shown below is the same circuit with the source turned on to **L1** and **L2.** L2 supplies voltage to one side of the relay coil and to one side of each light. R22 relay cannot energize until limit switch LS1 is closed. The **green** light will come on when the source L1 and L2 is turned on as there is a complete circuit to the **green** light through R22 normally closed contact. The green light will stay lit until the limit switch is closed.

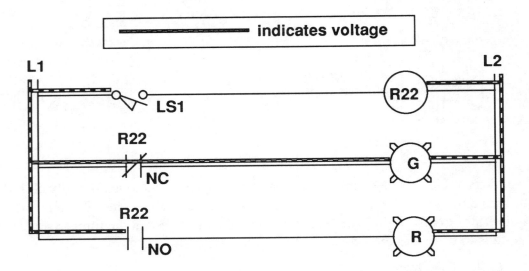

Shown below is the circuit with limit switch LS1 **closed**. When limit switch LS1 closes it completes the circuit to R22 relay. When R22 energizes it opens the normally closed contact which **opens** the circuit to the green light. At the same time when R22 relay energizes the normally open contact will **close** completing the circuit to the red light.

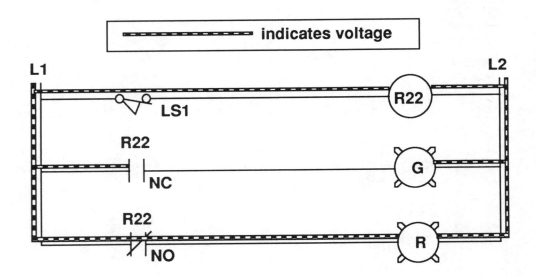

FLOAT SWITCH

The next circuit is a float switch that energizes a solenoid that opens a drain valve.

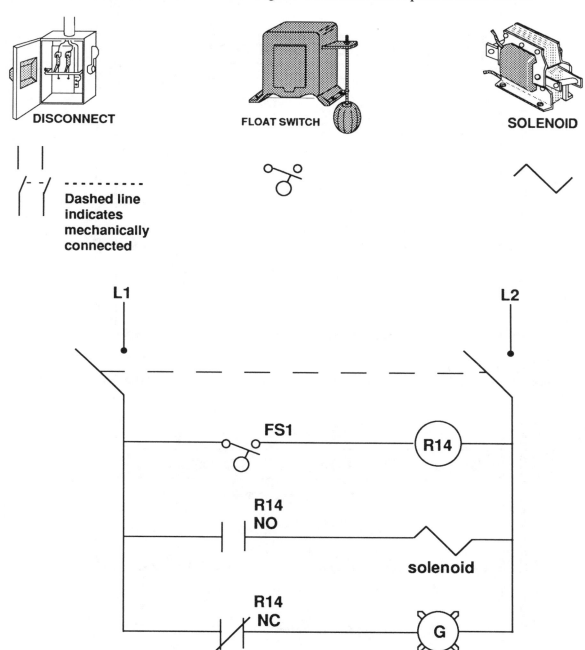

DISCONNECT

Dashed line indicates mechanically connected

FLOAT SWITCH

SOLENOID

L1

L2

FS1

R14

R14
NO

solenoid

R14
NC

G

When the disconnect is closed, L2 will flow to one side of the R14 coil, solenoid and light. L1 will flow to one side of float switch, R14 NO interlock and through R14 NC interlock to the light.

When the disconnect is closed, the green light is "ON". When the water level rises and closes the float switch, this will energize R14 relay and R14 NO will close energizing the solenoid opening a mechanical drain valve and at the same time R14 NC will open and the light will go "OFF". When the water level lowers, the float switch will open and the green light will come back "ON".

15

The circuit below shows the path of voltage at the first step, when the disconnect is closed.

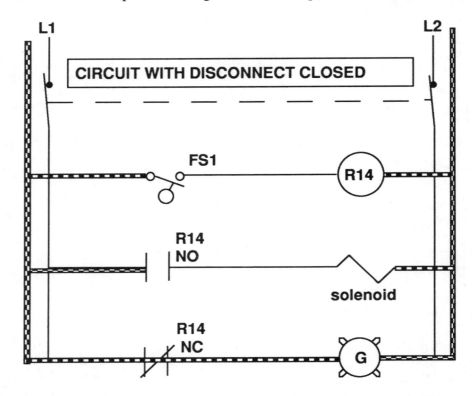

The circuit below shows the path of voltage when the water level rises and the float switch closes.

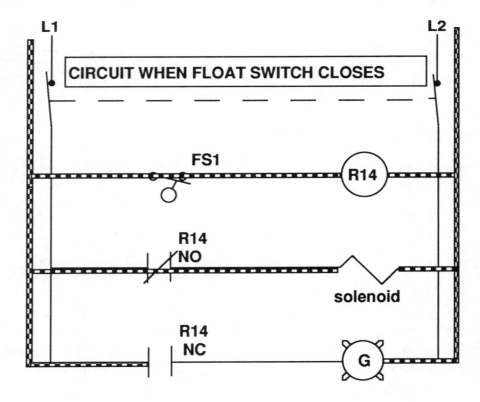

PRESSURE SWITCH

Lift stations, sump pumps, submersible pumps use different types of float switches for controls.

Sump pump

Submersible pump

The load can be **controlled** by many different devices such as single-pole switches, 3-way switches, limit switches, pressure switches, temperature switches, time-delay switches, foot switches, push-button switches, etc.

The circuit below is controlled by a pressure switch. When the pressure builds to a pre-set limit the pressure switch contact will close energizing R8 relay which will energize the alarm bell through R8 NO contact as it closes and the green light will shut off at the same time as R8 NC contact will open.

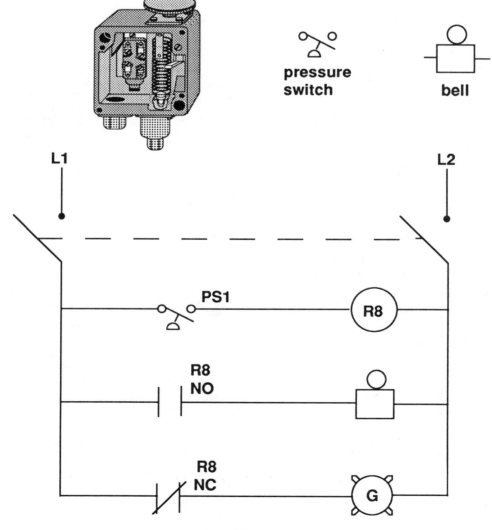

pressure switch

bell

2-WIRE CONTROL

The term "2-wire" control arises from the fact that the basic circuit requires only two wires to connect the controlling contact to the coil. The contact could be on a pressure switch, float switch, temperature switch, etc. which requires no operator as the contact is **automatically** closed by pressure, liquid, heat, etc.

If a power failure occurs while the contact of the device is closed, the coil will de-energize. When power is restored, the coil will energize **automatically** through the contact that is being held by pressure, liquid, heat, etc.

This can become a dangerous situation if the circuit is being used to start a machine where fingers and hands may be in the machine when it **automatically** starts when the power is restored again.

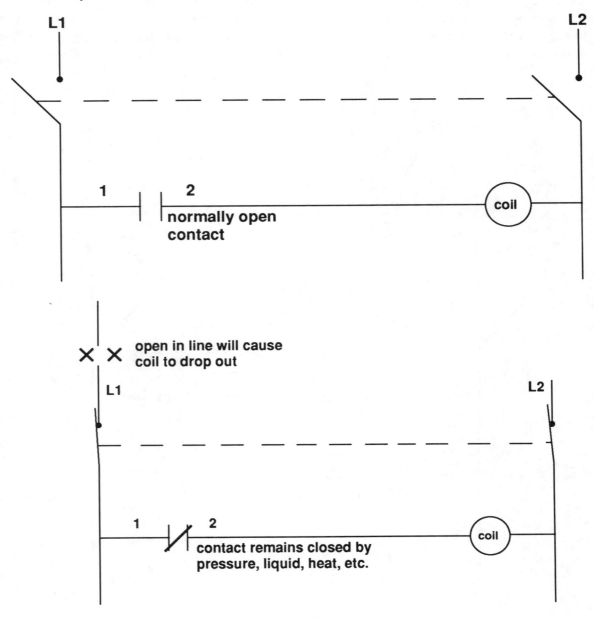

3-WIRE CONTROL

The term "3-wire" arises from the fact that the basic circuit requires at least three wires to connect the control devices to the coil.

The 3-wire control uses momentary contact push buttons or similar devices to energize the coil.

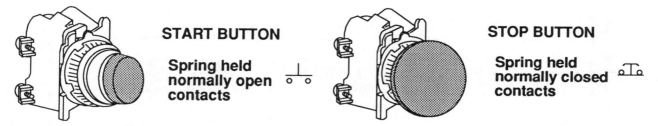

START BUTTON

Spring held normally open contacts

STOP BUTTON

Spring held normally closed contacts

The 3-wire control circuit is used to prevent the unexpected energizing of the coil which could result in possible injury to machine operators or damage to the machinery.

The coil is energized by pressing the start button. An auxiliary "holding circuit" normally open contact on the relay, forms a parallel circuit around the start button contacts keeping the coil energized after the start button is released. If a power failure occurs, the coil will de-energize and will open the holding circuit contact. When power is restored, the **start** button **must** be pressed before the coil will energize again, thus preventing unexpected starting of the machine.

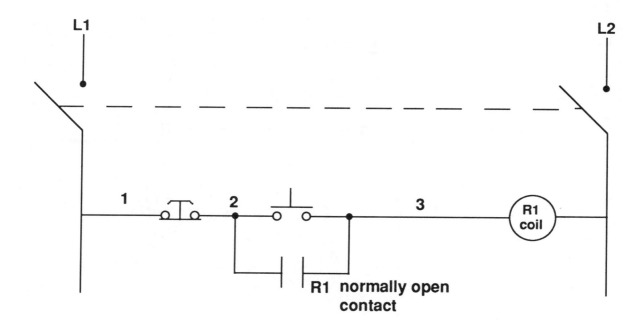

19

When the start button is pressed it completes the circuit energizing R1 coil. But, without a "holding circuit" R1 coil would de-energize when the start button is released. This would be a "jog" or "inch" type circuit.

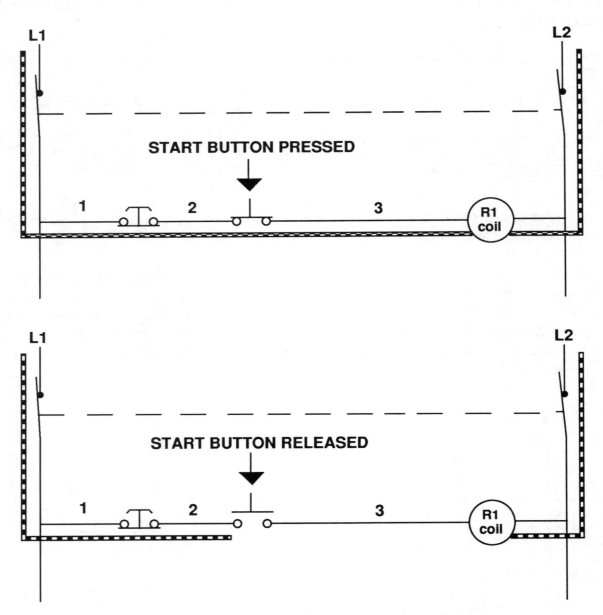

Shown below is a "holding circuit". R1 normally open contact has been connected in parallel with the start button so when the start button is released R1 coil is **held** energized through the R1 NO contact.

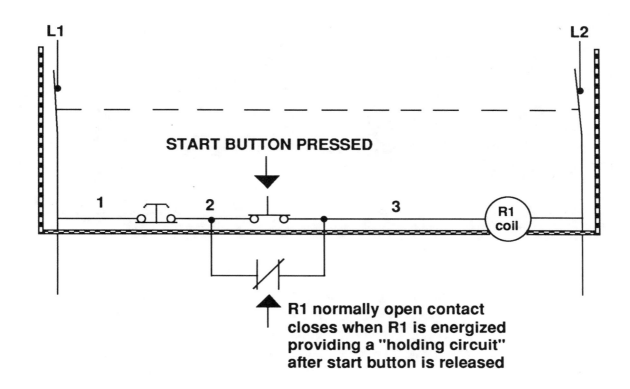

START BUTTON PRESSED

R1 normally open contact closes when R1 is energized providing a "holding circuit" after start button is released

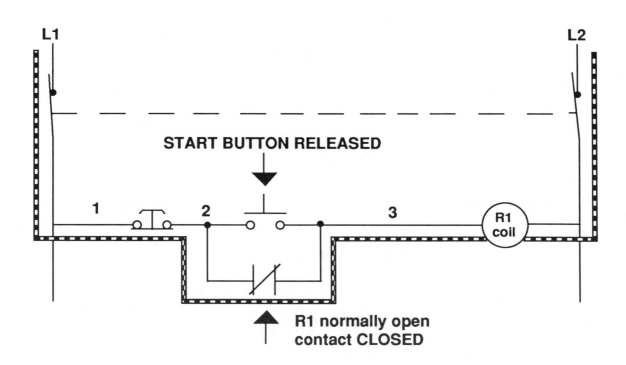

START BUTTON RELEASED

R1 normally open contact CLOSED

Shown below is a main wiring diagram showing the connections of stop-start push buttons controlling a relay with a light for a load.

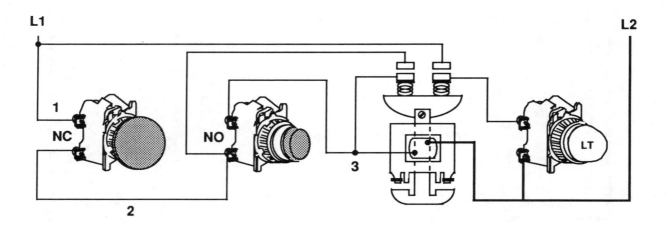

Shown below is the same circuit in a much easier to follow schematic diagram.

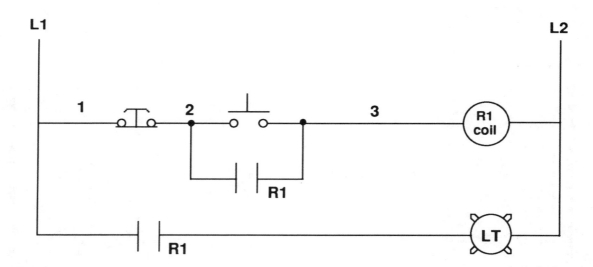

The light can be shut off from two different places by adding another stop button and connecting it in **series**. You can add as many stops as necessary as long as they are connected in series in the circuit.

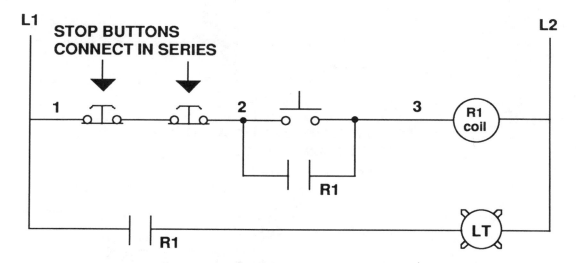

The circuit below shows the light can be turned on from three different locations and turned off from three locations. Start buttons connect in **parallel** as shown.

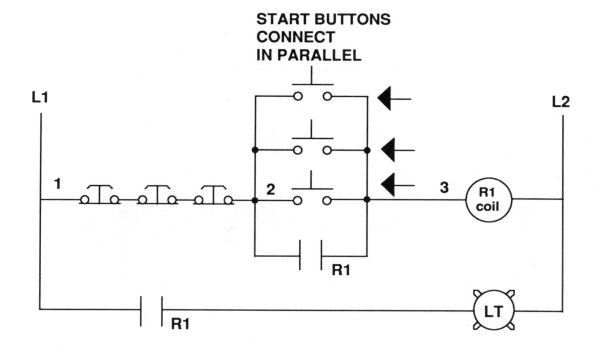

Shown below is an industrial machine with an air cylinder controlled electrically by push buttons, relays, limit switches and solenoids.

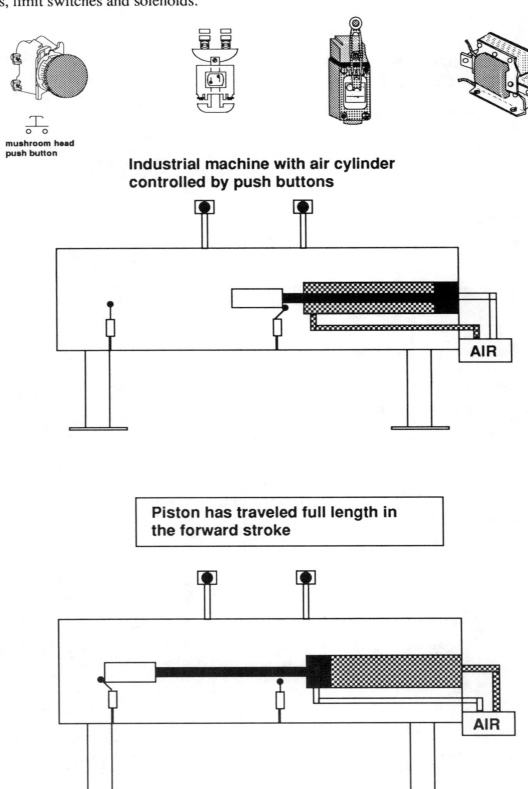

mushroom head push button

Industrial machine with air cylinder controlled by push buttons

AIR

Piston has traveled full length in the forward stroke

AIR

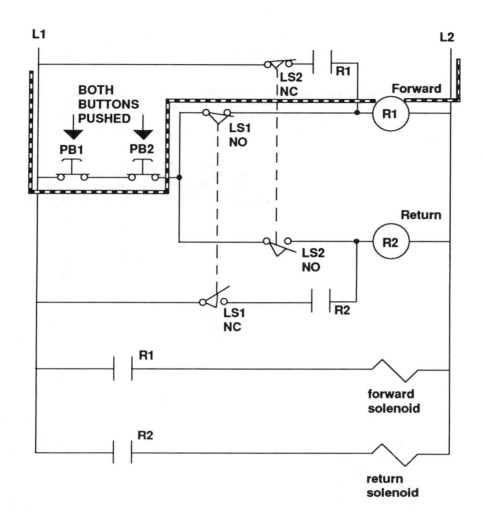

BOTH BUTTONS PUSHED

L1   L2

PB1   PB2

LS2 NC   R1   Forward   R1

LS1 NO

Return   R2

LS2 NO

LS1 NC   R2

R1   forward solenoid

R2   return solenoid

The air cylinder is in the NORMAL position with cylinder returned. LS1 NO contact is being HELD closed by the ram and LS1 NC contact is being HELD open by the ram.

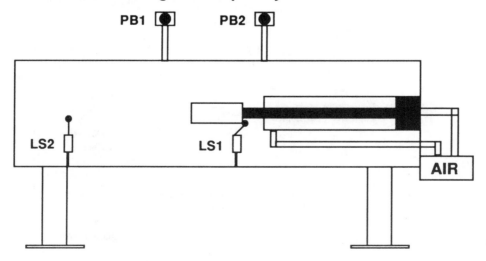

PB1   PB2

LS2   LS1   AIR

Piston has traveled full length in the forward stroke

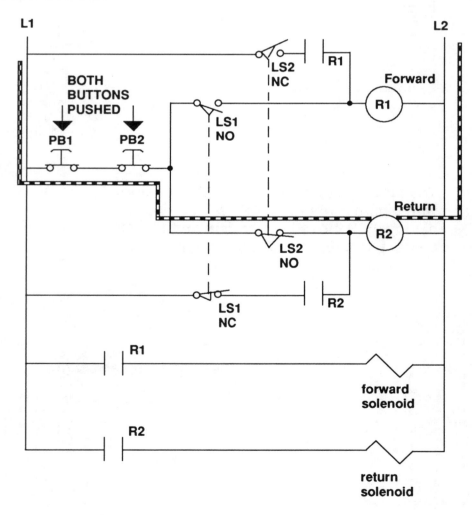

When the cylinder reaches its full stroke it makes contact with LS2 and **closes** the normally open contact which sets up the circuit for return by pressing both push buttons. R2 coil has a holding circuit through LS1 NC and R2 NO.

When the cylinder makes contact with LS1 it opens the LS1 NC contact which de-energizes R2 relay coil. When the cylinder makes contact with LS1 it also closes the LS1 NO contact which sets up the sequence of the machine for the next forward stroke.

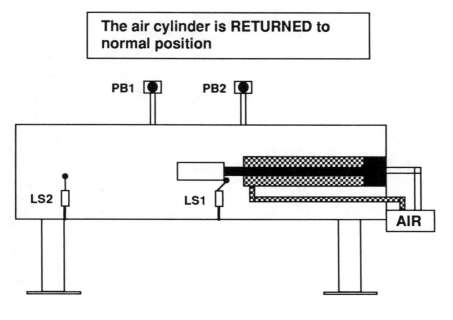

The air cylinder is RETURNED to normal position

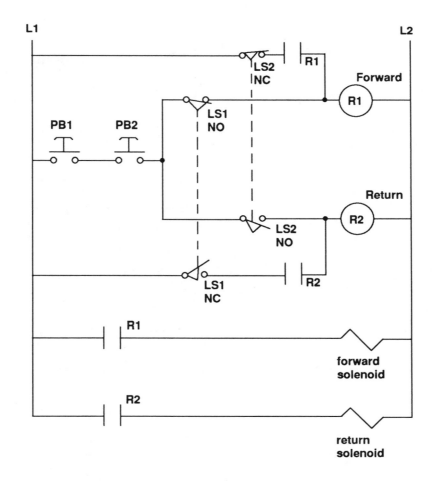

The circuit below has two push buttons connected in series so that **both** hands must be out of the machinery before the solenoid to an air valve can be energized. Both limit switches have a NO and a NC set of contacts. LS1 NO is **held** closed and LS1 NC is **held** open in the normal position of the air cylinder. When both push buttons are pressed R1 relay is energized through the LS1 NO contact, R1 relay has a holding circuit through LS2 NC and R1 NO. When the air cylinder reaches its full stroke it will open LS2 NC and will de-energize R1 coil. LS1 NO is open and LS1 NC is closed with the air cylinder is this position. To **return** the air cylinder, press both push buttons and R2 relay is energized through LS2 NO contact, R2 relay has a holding circuit through LS1 NC and R2 NO. When the air cylinder returns to the normal position it will open LS1 NC and de-energize R2 coil.

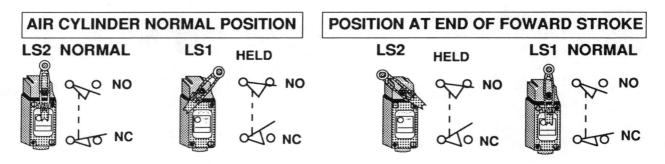

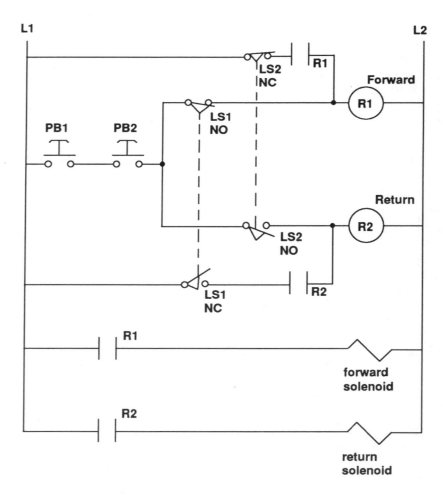

28

TIMING RELAYS

Timing relays are used in automatic control circuits such as controls for machine tools and to control the sequence of operation of the machine. Timing relays are also used for motor speed acceleration.

There are 3 categories of timers: Dashpot timers, synchronous clock timers and electronic timers.

CLOCK TIMER

The magnetic coil operated dashpot-type timing relay is either fluid (oil or silicone) or pneumatic (air) operated. Pneumatic timers are not affected by temperature changes and have a better repeat accuracy than the oil dashpot timers. Temperature changes have an affect on the oil which will affect the timing of the dashpot.

In some cases a synchronous clock timer or a solid state timer could be used instead of a pneumatic timer. The operation of the pneumatic timer will be explained on the following pages because it is the easiest to understand in terms of mechanical operation.

The pneumatic timing relay time-delay function depends upon the transfer of air through a restricted orifice by use of a rubber diaphragm.

The timing range is adjustable by turning a knob to increase or decrease the time it takes for the contacts to open or close. A needle valve is used to vary the amount of orifice restriction. The timing range can be adjusted from two seconds to thirty seconds.

Timing relays provide two types of time delay. The first type is called an **on-delay**, which means when the relay coil is **energized** it provides a time delay to the contacts. The second type of time delay is called an **off-delay**, which means when the relay coil is **de-energized** it provides a time delay to the contacts.

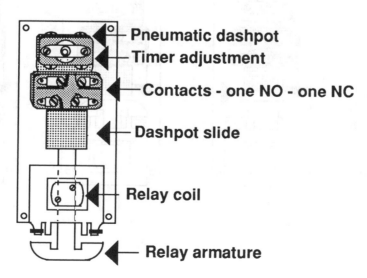

- Pneumatic dashpot
- Timer adjustment
- Contacts - one NO - one NC
- Dashpot slide
- Relay coil
- Relay armature

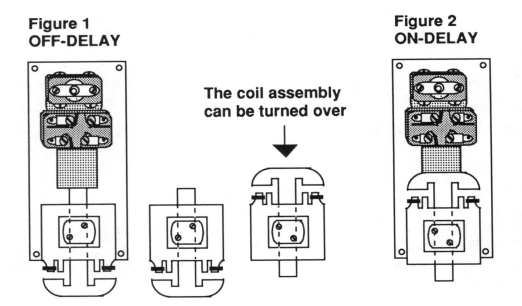

**Figure 1
OFF-DELAY**

**The coil assembly
can be turned over**

**Figure 2
ON-DELAY**

Shown below is an **ON-DELAY** timing relay. When the relay coil is energized the armature pulls down and away from the dashpot slide. The timer adjustment which opens and closes the size of the orifice will determine how long it takes for the dashpot slide to reach the bottom of its travel. When the slide reaches the bottom the contacts will change position and complete the **timed** circuit to the load.

Relay coil is ENERGIZED

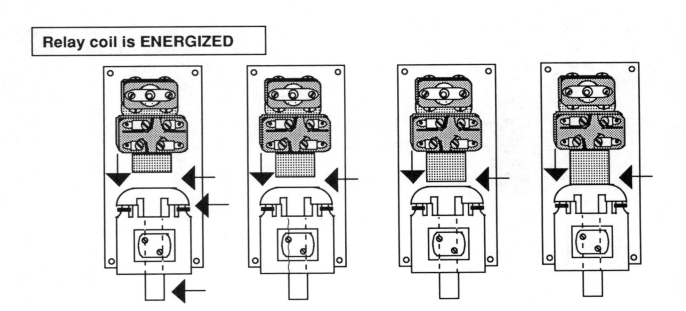

```
┌─────────────────────────────────────────────────┐
│                    SYMBOLS                        │
│                 TIMED CONTACTS                    │
│        Contact action is delayed after coil is:   │
│                                                   │
│      ┌──────────────┐     ┌──────────────┐        │
│      │  ENERGIZED   │     │ DE-ENERGIZED │        │
│      └──────────────┘     └──────────────┘        │
│                                                   │
│   N.O.T.C.      N.C.T.O.      N.O.T.O.    N.C.T.C.│
│                                                   │
│   normally      normally      normally    normally│
│   open          closed        open        closed  │
│   timed         timed         timed       timed   │
│   then          then          then        then    │
│   closes        opens         opens       closes  │
└─────────────────────────────────────────────────┘
```

normally
open

normally
closed

┌─────────────────────────────┐   ┌─────────────────────────────┐
│   coil   │   │   coil   │
│   energized   │   │   de-energized   │
│   │   │   │
│   │   │   │
│   N.O.T.C.   N.C.T.O.   │   │   N.O.T.O.   N.C.T.C.   │
│   │   │   │
│   │   │   │
│   normally   normally   │   │   normally   normally   │
│   open   closed   │   │   open   closed   │
│   timed   timed   │   │   timed   timed   │
│   then   then   │   │   then   then   │
│   closes   opens   │   │   opens   closes   │
│   │   │   │
│   │   │   │
└─────────────────────────────┘   │   │
                                    └─────────────────────────────┘

31

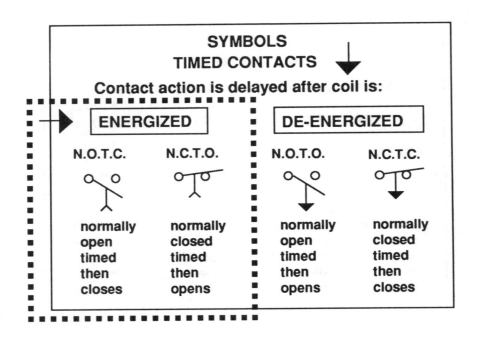

SYMBOLS
TIMED CONTACTS

Contact action is delayed after coil is:

ENERGIZED		DE-ENERGIZED	
N.O.T.C.	**N.C.T.O.**	**N.O.T.O.**	**N.C.T.C.**
normally open timed then closes	normally closed timed then opens	normally open timed then opens	normally closed timed then closes

Figure 1 below shows the coil **energized** and the position of the contacts on the relay. When the dashpot slide reaches the bottom of its travel the position of the relay contacts change as they have **timed** out.

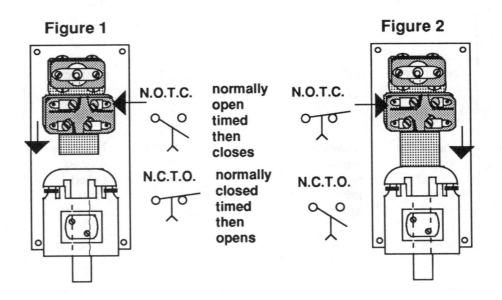

Figure 1

N.O.T.C. — normally open timed then closes

N.C.T.O. — normally closed timed then opens

Figure 2

N.O.T.C.

N.C.T.O.

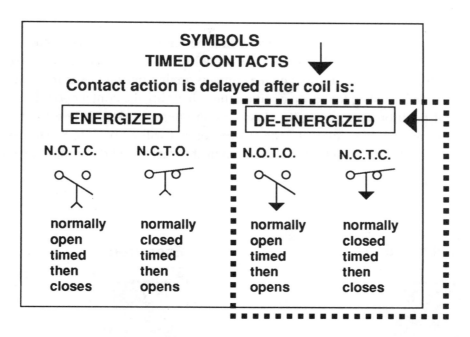

SYMBOLS
TIMED CONTACTS

Contact action is delayed after coil is:

ENERGIZED		DE-ENERGIZED	
N.O.T.C.	**N.C.T.O.**	**N.O.T.O.**	**N.C.T.C.**
normally open timed then closes	normally closed timed then opens	normally open timed then opens	normally closed timed then closes

Shown below is an **OFF-DELAY** timing relay. When the relay coil is **de-energized** a time delay will be provided. The contact arrangement shown above for **de-energized** becomes confusing for some students as it reads the **normally open** contact after it **times out** becomes **normally open**.

Note the relay armature assembly is **reversed** from the position used in the ON-DELAY where the coil was energized to start the timing action.

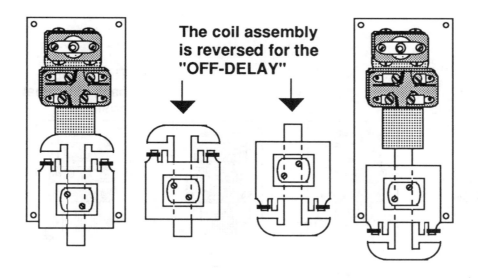

The coil assembly is reversed for the "OFF-DELAY"

What you must realize is the **relay coil** must first be **energized** and then when it becomes **de-energized** the timing sequence will start. As shown below is the normal **de-energized** position the dashpot slide has traveled to the bottom and the contacts are in **normal position**. When the relay coil is energized the slide is pushed to the top position thus changing the contact position from **normally open** to a closed position and **normally closed** to an open position. When the relay coil is **de-energized** it will start the time delay and the closed contact will go back to **normally open** and the open contact will go back to **normally closed** when the dashpot slide completes its travel to the bottom.

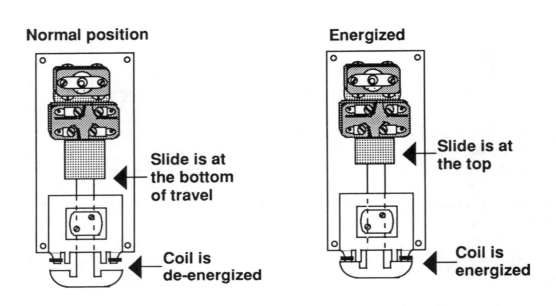

Normal position

Slide is at
the bottom
of travel

Coil is
de-energized

Energized

Slide is at
the top

Coil is
energized

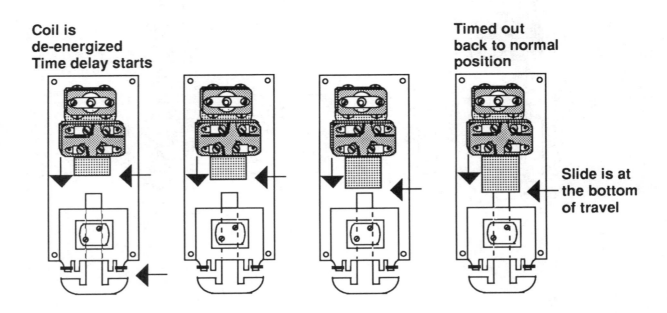

**Coil is
de-energized
Time delay starts**

**Timed out
back to normal
position**

Slide is at
the bottom
of travel

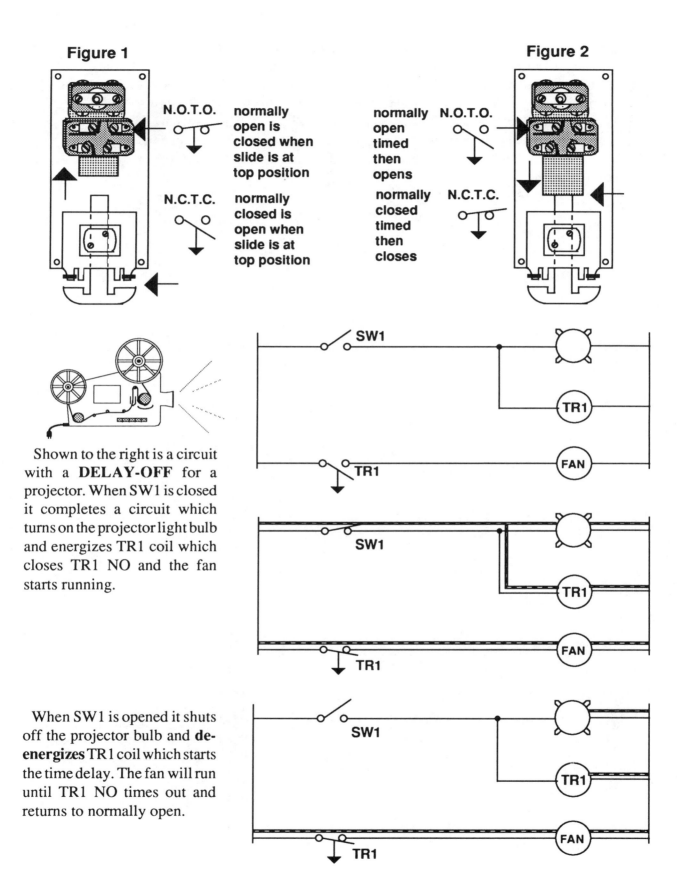

Figure 1

N.O.T.O. normally open is closed when slide is at top position

N.C.T.C. normally closed is open when slide is at top position

Figure 2

normally open timed then opens N.O.T.O.

normally closed timed then closes N.C.T.C.

SW1

TR1

FAN

TR1

SW1

TR1

FAN

TR1

SW1

TR1

FAN

TR1

Shown to the right is a circuit with a **DELAY-OFF** for a projector. When SW1 is closed it completes a circuit which turns on the projector light bulb and energizes TR1 coil which closes TR1 NO and the fan starts running.

When SW1 is opened it shuts off the projector bulb and **de-energizes** TR1 coil which starts the time delay. The fan will run until TR1 NO times out and returns to normally open.

Shown below is an example of an **ON-DELAY** circuit. When the float switch FS1 is closed due to high water level, R1 relay coil will energize closing the normally open R1 relay contacts completing the circuit to the solenoid coil and the timing relay coil TR1. The solenoid operates a drain valve to lower the water level. As the water level is lowering the timing relay is also timing out. The water is to reach the low level within 30 seconds which will open the float switch FS1 and de-energize the timing relay TR1 and the warning bell will not sound. If the drain is plugged or slow in draining this allows the timing relay to complete its 30 second timing cycle and TR1 interlock will close which energizes the warning bell.

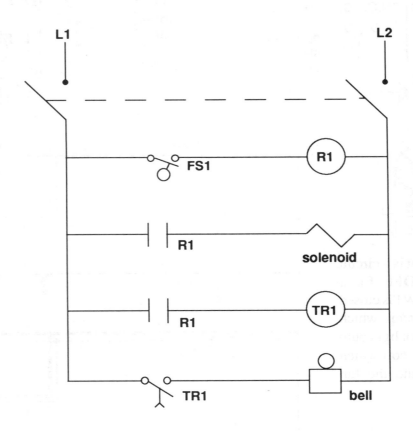

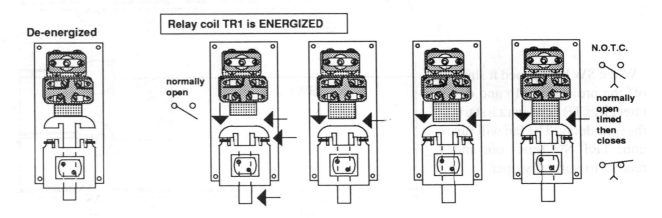

De-energized

Relay coil TR1 is ENERGIZED

normally open

N.O.T.C.

normally open timed then closes

36

The circuit below shows two timers with a relay to control solenoids to an air cylinder. The timers can control the cylinders stroke and keep the machine running automatically.

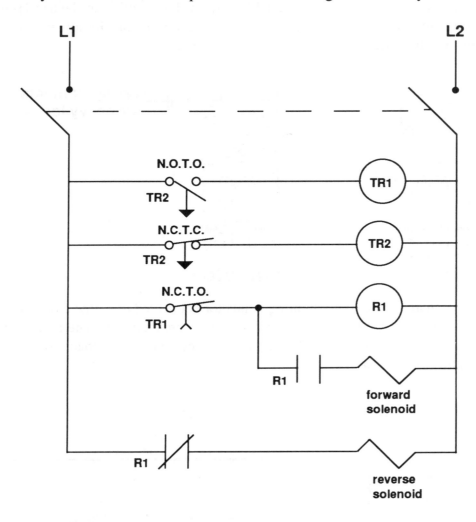

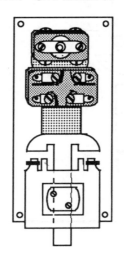

TR1 ON-DELAY

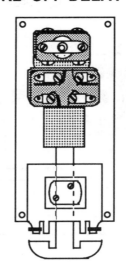

TR2 OFF-DELAY

CONTACTORS

Contactors are devices used for repeatedly establishing and interrupting an electrical **power** circuit. Contactors are used to switch **heavier loads** such as lighting and heating. Relays are used as auxiliary devices to control **light loads** such as coils, pilot lights, etc.

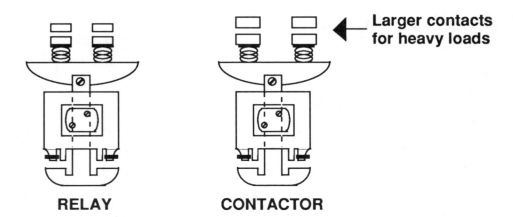

Larger contacts for heavy loads

RELAY   **CONTACTOR**

Shown below is an application of a lighting contactor connected to a time clock. The contact on the time clock is small, as the only current is that of the contactor coil. The main contacts to the lighting loads are larger than those of a relay, as there may be several light loads connected to several contacts on a lighting contactor.

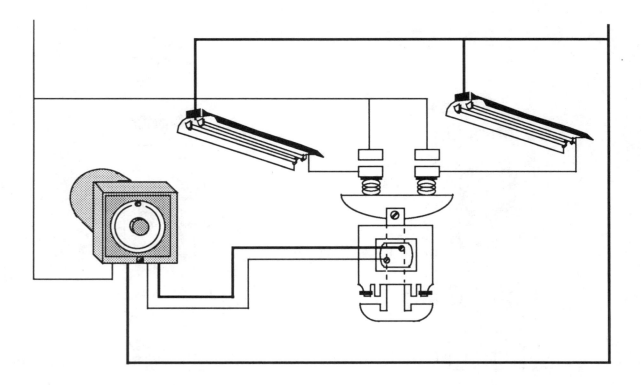

38

MOTOR STARTERS

It has been stated that 85% of industrial machines are driven by motors. A motor is "dumb", it has no intelligence and will attempt to drive any load, even if excessive. A motor must be protected from destroying itself. A locked rotor that exists when a motor is so heavily loaded that the motor shaft cannot turn will draw excessive current until the motor is burnt up if not disconnected from the line voltage.

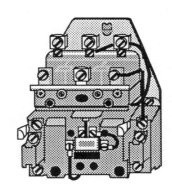

The difference between a motor circuit and a lighting or appliance circuit is the motor must start up from a standstill to a full run position when the circuit is turned on. The motor draws a tremendous amount of inrush current when it starts up, usually six to eight times the amount of the normal running current. To avoid tripping the circuit breaker or blowing the fuse on the starting of the motor, a higher rated fuse or circuit breaker is used.

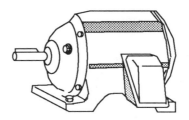

Example, a household clothes dryer is shown connected to a 30 amp circuit breaker.

30 AMP

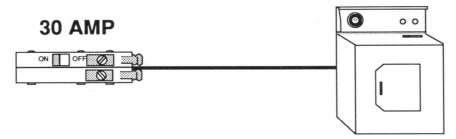

A 28 amp motor has a 70 amp circuit breaker. The breaker is sized at 250% of the 28 amps.

70 AMP

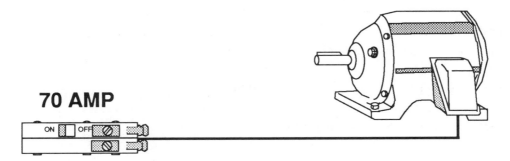

When the branch circuit breaker or fuse is sized large enough to carry the starting current of the motor it will rarely protect the motor against damage caused by an overload that continues for some time. Therefore a separate overload protective device must be installed to protect the motor from **overloads**.

All motors require overload protection if **automatically started**. The Code permits manually controlled **portable** (not permanently installed) motors rated 1 hp or less to be protected by the branch circuit breaker or fuse.

Thermal overload protector

Often these smaller motors have a motor overload device built into the motor (integral overload device), it's the red button on the end bell housing, called a "thermal protector".

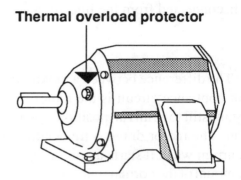

If a motor is permanently installed and not provided with integral (built-in) protection, separate overload protection must be provided. Most likely you will use "heater coils" that are installed inside the motor starter.

What most electrician's call the motor starter is actually the motor controller. It can be the manual type or the magnetic coil type like a relay.

The motor starter serves as the controller as well as the overload protective device. It must never serve as the disconnecting means.

DISCONNECT

A motor controller (starter) is a device used to start and stop the motor, interrupt the stalled-rotor current of the motor and other types of overloads, reverse the motor, control its speed, etc.

A motor control circuit is the wires from a motor controller to a device such as a push button station. The motor control circuit does not carry the main power current to the motor. It carries the small signal current to energize the coil of the magnetic starter.

There is a difference between motor over**current** protection and motor over**load** protection.

The overcurrent device (breaker or fuse) is to protect the motor branch circuit conductors, control apparatus and motor from **short circuits or ground faults**.

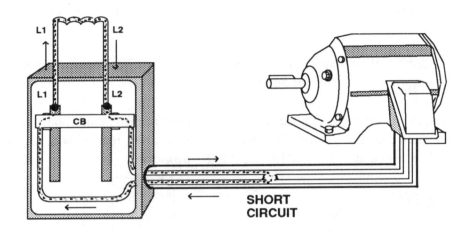

Overcurrents due to short circuits or ground faults **are a much higher amperage** than the locked rotor currents in an overload condition.

The Code requires a means to disconnect the motor and controller from the line. A circuit breaker can provide both short circuit, ground fault protection and a disconnect in one basic device. Whereas a fuse that is used for overcurrent protection must also include a disconnect switch in the circuit.

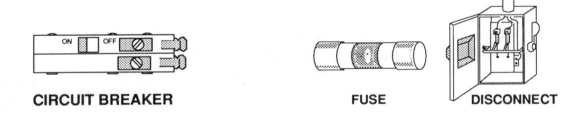

CIRCUIT BREAKER   **FUSE**   **DISCONNECT**

The 20 amp rating of the branch circuit is thermal current, not the destructive high currents that occur during a ground-fault or short-circuit condition. Electrical conductors and equipment have current withstand ratings generally based on the overcurrent device (fuse or circuit breaker) opening the circuit within the first one-half cycle, which is 8 thousandths of a second. The ICEA lists the maximum short-circuit withstand rating for a #12 copper wire at **3800 amperes** for one-half cycle. A #12 copper wire can withstand 1550 amperes for 3 cycles, but remember, 60 cycles is still only **one second** in time.

Many electricians don't realize that a 20 amp rated circuit with #12 conductors must be capable of carrying thousands of amperes of current during a fault.

Example; the branch circuit cable is accidentally cut 6 feet from the panelboard thus practically eliminating the resistance of the circuit. The only resistance is 12 feet of wire. 1.93Ω x .012' = .02316Ω. Current flow, I = E/R = 120v/.02316Ω = **5181 amperes.**

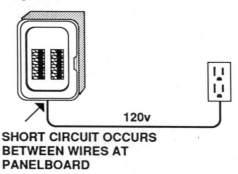

**SHORT CIRCUIT OCCURS
BETWEEN WIRES AT
PANELBOARD**

If the short-circuit occurred inside the panelboard with only 6 feet of wire, the resistance would be 1.93Ω x .006' = .01158Ω. Current flow, I = E/R = 120v/.01158Ω = **10,362 amperes.**

That's why the circuit breaker has an interrupting rating stamped on the side, **"10,000 amperes"**.

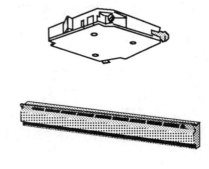

Example; the current flowing through an electric heater at a **high** resistance creates heat. The voltage (pressure) is pushing the flow of current through the high resistance. When a short-circuit fault occurs it offers a **new path** of **less resistance** so the voltage (pressure) doesn't have to push as hard and the current **flow** increases tremendously as there is no opposition (resistance) to its flow.

The high current will open the inverse-time circuit breaker quickly. Inverse-time means, the higher the current the quicker it will open.

Opening the circuit breaker is like shutting off the water pump. The pressure is turned off.

Now you can see how the steel in your pliers melts when you cut into a hot circuit. Steel melts at approximately 2500° F. Remember, 20 amps flowing in a circuit won't melt steel. As you can see by using Ohm's Law, we are talking about much higher currents than the 20 amperes for a #12 wire.

OVERLOADS

Overloads can be electrical as well as mechanical, in origin. Low voltage or single phasing of a three phase system are examples of electrical overloads. Mechanical overloads can come from a high head pressure on a pump, a bearing on a shaft freezing up, etc.

The effect of an **overload** is a rise in temperature in the motor windings. The larger the overload, the more quickly the temperature will increase to the point of damaging the insulation and lubrication of the motor bearings. It has an inverse effect, the higher the current in a given time, the shorter the time before motor damage occurs.

All **overloads** shorten the life of a motor by deteriorating the motor insulation. The intensive heat concentration generated by excessive current in the motor windings is what causes the insulation to fail and burn up the motor.

It has been estimated that for every 1°C rise over **normal** ambient temperatures, it can reduce the life of the motor one year for each degree above the insulation rating. The **normal** rating for most motors is 40°C which is 104°F. Ambient temperature is the temperature surrounding the motor, the environment where the motor is placed.

Fuses are not designed to provide over**load** protection. Their basic function is to provide protection against short circuits and ground faults, the over**current** protection. A single element fuse chosen on the basis of motor full load current would blow every time the motor is started. On the other hand, if a fuse were chosen large enough to pass the starting (inrush) current, it would not protect the motor from overloads. A dual element or time delay fuse can provide motor overload protection, but the disadvantange is, if the fuse blows it must be replaced.

The **overload relay** is the heart of motor protection. Like the dual element fuse, the overload relay holds during the starting period (inrush current), yet provides protection on small overloads above the full load current of the motor when it's running. Unlike the dual element fuse, the overload relay can withstand repeated trip and reset cycles without having to be replaced. The overload relay does **not** provide short circuit or ground fault protection, that is the function of a breaker or fuse, **not** the overload relay.

The **overload relay** consists of a current sensing unit connected in the conductor to the motor, plus a mechanism, actuated by the sensing unit, which serves directly or indirectly to break open the circuit. In a manual motor starter an overload trips a mechanical latch causing the power contacts to the motor to open. In a magnetic (coil) starter an overload opens a set of contacts within the overload relay itself. These contacts are wired in **series** with the coil of the motor starter. When the coil de-energizes it opens the power contacts to the motor.

Overload relays can be classified as being either **thermal** or **magnetic**. Magnetic overload relays react only to excess current and are not affected by temperature. The device operates through the use of a **current coil**. At a specified overcurrent value, the current coil acts as a solenoid, causing a set of normally closed contacts to open thus disconnecting the motor from the circuit.

An advantage of the magnetic overload relay is that it is extremely quick on reset, since it does not require a cooling off period before it can be reset. The disadvantage of the magnetic overload relay is that it is more expensive that the thermal overload relay. The thermal overload relay is the one most often used.

Thermal overload relays rely on the rising temperatures caused by the excessive current and trip the overload mechanism when the maximum temperature is reached. Thermal overload relays can be subdivided into **two** types, the **melting alloy** (solder pot) and **bi-metallic**.

The **melting alloy** thermal overload relay is also referred to as the "solder pot relay". With this overload relay the motor current passes through a small heater winding (heater coil). Under overload conditions the heat **causes a special solder to melt**, allowing a ratchet wheel to spin free, opening the interlock contacts that are wired in series with the coil in a magnetic motor starter. When this occurs, the overload relay is said to have "tripped". The heat transfer characteristic and the accuracy of the heater coil cannot be accidentally changed. Thermal overload heater coils are rated in amperes and are selected on the basis of the motor full load current, not the horsepower of the motor. To obtain appropriate tripping current for motors of different sizes, or different full load currents, a range of thermal units (heaters) are available.

Heater separate

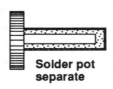
Solder pot separate

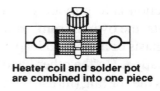
Heater coil and solder pot are combined into one piece

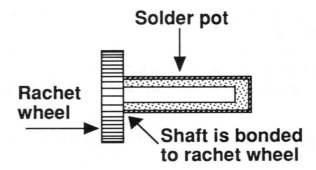

Solder pot

Rachet wheel

Shaft is bonded to rachet wheel

44

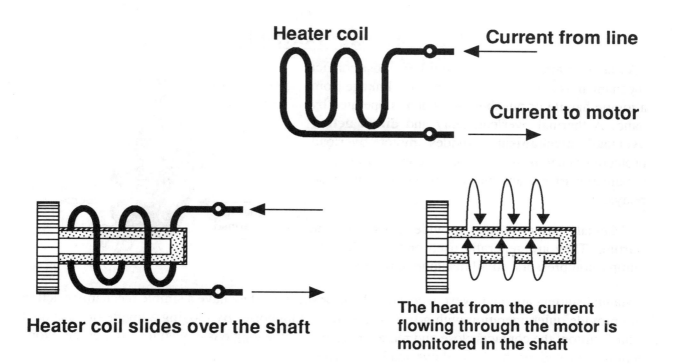

Heater coil — **Current from line**

Current to motor

Heater coil slides over the shaft

The heat from the current flowing through the motor is monitored in the shaft

Shown below is a sketch of the current flowing from the line through the heater coil and on to the motor. The solder pot is monitoring the amount of heat from the current flow. This application would be for a **manual starter** as the **line** current would be interrupted in tripped condition.

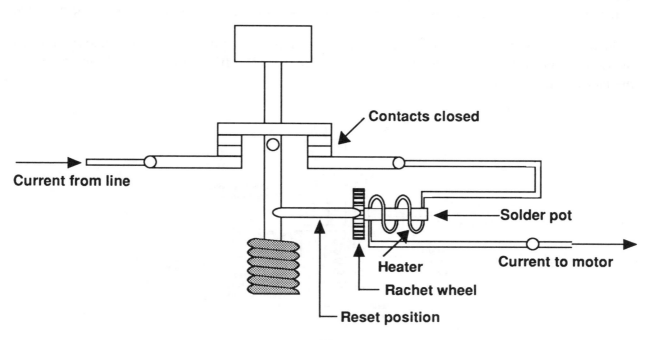

Contacts closed

Current from line

Solder pot

Current to motor

Heater

Rachet wheel

Reset position

45

MANUAL STARTER

A manual starter is a motor controller whose contact mechanism is operated by a mechanical linkage from a toggle handle or pushbutton, which is operated by hand. A thermal overload relay and **direct acting overload mechanism** provides motor overload protection and will interrupt the line contact. Basically, a manual starter is an "on-off" switch with overload relays.

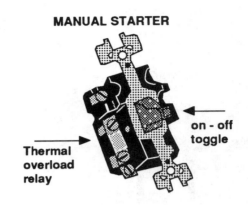

MANUAL STARTER

on - off toggle

Thermal overload relay

Manual starters usually provide across the line starting. They are generally used on fans, blowers, pumps, compressors, small machine tools, etc.

Manual starters are the lowest in cost of all motor starters. They have a simple mechanism action and provide quiet operation with no ac magnet humming noise. By moving a toggle or pushing a "start" button, the contacts close and remain closed until the toggle is moved to "off", or the "stop" button is pushed, or the thermal overload relay trips.

The advantage of using a manual starter for exhaust fans, pumps, compressors, oil burners, etc. is if power fails, the contacts remain closed, and when power is restored the motor will start again without having to manually push the toggle or start button again. This is good to keep in mind with an industrial building that has several fan motors. Manual starters save the maintenance person from having to start each motor in the building when power is restored.

Keep in mind the **restarting** of a motor when power is restored can also be a **disadvantage**. A manual starter should **not** be used where a machine operator may have his fingers or hands involved in the operation of a machine. When power is restored it could cause an accident. The 3-wire magnetic coil starter would be used in this case requiring the operator to push a button to restart the machine.

Shown below is the **tripped** position of a manual starter. The contacts cannot be reclosed until the overload relay has been reset by moving the handle to the full "off" position, after allowing time for the thermal unit to cool.

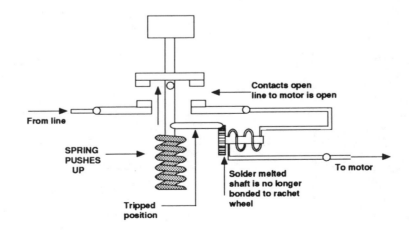

From line

Contacts open line to motor is open

SPRING PUSHES UP

Tripped position

Solder melted shaft is no longer bonded to rachet wheel

To motor

BIMETALLIC OVERLOAD

The other type of overload relay is the **bimetallic.** The bimetallic thermal overload relays employ a U-shape bimetal strip, associated with a current carrying heater element. When an overload occurs, the heat will cause the bimetal to warp and open a contact.

The bimetallic overload relay can be hand reset or automatic reset. However, automatic reset overload relays should not normally be used with 2-wire control circuits. The reason is, when the overload relay contacts reclose after an overload relay trip, the motor will restart, and, unless the cause of the overload has been removed, the overload will trip again. This cycle of tripping and resetting will continue till eventually the motor will burn up. More important is the danger of restarting when personnel are involved as mentioned earlier. The unexpected restarting of a machine may find the operator in a hazardous situation.

Shown below is the motor circuit in normal position and when an overload has occured with a bimetallic overload relay.

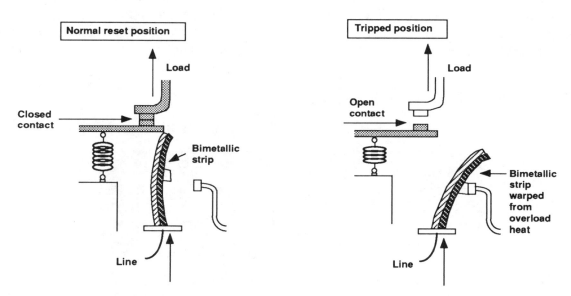

Ambient-compensated bimetallic overload relays were designed for one particular situation; that is, when the motor is at a constant temperature and the motor controller is located separately in a varying temperature. In this case, if a standard thermal overload relay were used, it would not trip consistently at the same level of the motor current if the motor controller temperature changed. This thermal overload relay is always affected by the surrounding temperature. To compensate for the temperature variations the motor controller may see, an ambient temperature-compensated overload relay is applied. Its trip point is **not** affected by temperature and it performs consistently at the same value of current.

Melting alloy (solder pot) and bimetallic overload relays are designed to approximate the heat actually generated in the motor.

Heater coils will not detect high ambient temperatures at the motor location because they are monitoring line current. The high ambient temperatures at the motor location can burn the motor up without being detected.

TEMPERATURE RISE

As you can see by now, heat plays a very important role in motor protection. Both motor controllers and motors are subject to a 40°C (104°F) ambient temperature **limit**. This is the temperature **outside** the motor, not inside.

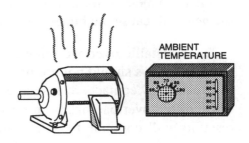

Current passing through the windings of a motor results in an increase in the motor temperature. The difference between the winding temperature of the motor when running and the ambient temperature is called the **temperature rise**.

The temperature rise produced at full load is not harmful provided the motor ambient temperature does not exceed 40°C (104°F).

Higher temperatures caused by increased current or higher ambient temperatures produces a deteriorating effect on the motor insulation and lubrication. An old "rule of thumb" states that for each increase of 10°C above rated temperature the motor life is cut in half.

When a Celsius thermometer reads 30°C, a Fahrenheit thermometer will read 86°F. Or when a Celsius reads 40°C, a Fahrenheit will read 104°F.

40° Celsius = 104° Fahrenheit

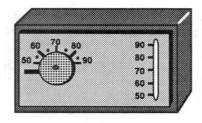
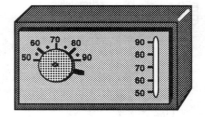

Temperature **RISE** is over and above the ambient temperature while the motor is delivering its rated horsepower. An ordinary motor is based on a temperature **rise** of 40°C which is a **rise** of 72°F. Don't confuse a **change** in the reading of the two different thermometers with their **actual** readings. When a Celsius changes from 40°C to 80°C (a 40°C rise), the Fahrenheit changes from 104°F to 176°F (a 72°F rise). One degree **rise** on the Celsius scale is the equivalent of 1.8° on the Fahrenheit scale.

Example, a 30°C (86°F) **rises** to 40°C (104°F) a 10°C rise. 10°C x 1.8 factor = 18°F. 86°F + 18°F = 104°F.

A 40°C **rise** is a 72°F rise. 104°F ambient + 72°F rise = 176°F actual heat. In a pump house or other closed in areas where the ambient is expected to exceed 104°F, a 50°C rise motor should be selected.

SERVICE FACTOR

If the motor manufacturer has given the motor a **service factor**, it means that the motor can be allowed to develop **more** than its rated or nameplate horsepower, without causing undue deterioration of the insulation. Example, a 10 hp motor has a service factor of 1.15, the motor can be allowed to develop 11.5 horsepower (10 hp x 1.15 service factor = 11.5 hp). The service factor depends on the motor design.

Over the years, better insulation on the wires used to wind the motors has been developed so the motor will not be damaged by the temperatures that would have destroyed older motors. This has reduced the physical size of todays motors. Todays motors run hotter without damaging the motor.

Remember, a 10 hp motor with a service factor can develop 11.5 hp without insulation damage providing the ambient temperature does not exceed 40°C or 104°F. A motor will operate longer and more efficiently if not used over its **rated** horsepower. The service factor provides **temporary** extra power if needed.

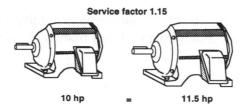

Service factor 1.15

10 hp = 11.5 hp

When selecting the size of overload relay heaters, the full load current of the motor, type of motor, and the possible difference in ambient temperature between the motor controller and the motor must all be taken into account. Always refer to the **nameplate** rating on the motor for the full load current.

When taking electrical exams, the full load current is determined from the Code Tables 430-148 for single-phase motors and Table 430-150 for three-phase motors, unless the **nameplate** rating is given in the exam question.

To size the heaters, Code section 430-32 is for continuous-duty motors more than one horsepower.

Heater

430-32a1 - A separate overload device that is responsive to motor current. This device shall be selected to trip or rated at no more than the following percent of the motor nameplate full load current rating.

Motors with a marked service factor not less than 1.15 ...... 125%
Motors with a marked temperature rise not over 40°C 125%
All other motors 115%

Example; a standard squirrel cage motor with no service factor or temperature rise markings that has a nameplate full load current rating of 12 amps would have the overload heater sized at 12 amps x 115% = **13.8 amps.**

49

With the heater sized to 13.8 amps with the motor full load current of 12 amps, a 1.8 amp increase in current will trip the overload.

At first when you see a 28 amp motor on a circuit that has a 70 amp circuit breaker you feel the circuit is not protected properly. But the truth is, it's just the opposite.

70 AMP

With thermal overload protection the motor is the best protected circuit.

A motor with a full load current of 28 amps would require a #10THW conductor. The overload protection would be 28 amps x 115% = 32.2. The overload trips out at 32.2 amps, a #10THW has an ampacity of 35 amps. The 70 amp circuit breaker is to allow the heavy inrush currents when starting and to protect against short circuits and ground faults.

The overload protection is the difference between a motor circuit and a lighting, appliance or receptacle circuit.

Example, the table lamp in the living room of your home generally has a #16 gauge cord wire or smaller. This lamp could be plugged into a 20 amp rated branch circuit.

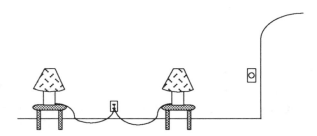

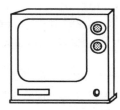

The living room is not a heavy loaded circuit, with the television turned on and a couple of lamps the current flowing would be around 4 amps. The lamp cord would have to increase 18 to 20 amps before the circuit breaker would trip or the fuse would blow. The overcurrent device has to do **both**, protect against short circuits, ground faults **and overloads**.

Two functions - overcurrent and overload protection

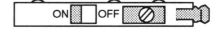

With a motor circuit, the breaker provides overcurrent protection and the heater provides overload protection.

Overcurrent   Overload

50

CURRENT TRANSFORMER

With larger motors, a current transformer is used so the heater is not gigantic in size. The current transformer has a ratio of 250 to 5. The output of a standard current transformer is five amps maximum.

Example; a 200 hp three-phase motor with a full load current of 500 amps with CT's would have a heater sized at 10 amps. 50 to 1 ratio.

CURRENT TRANSFORMER DOUGHNUT TYPE

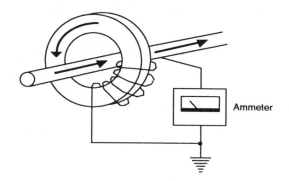

Ammeter

Current transformers are standard on size 5 and larger starters. Size 5 starts at 75 hp.

Code section 250-121 requires grounding of CT's connected to circuits of 300 volts and over.

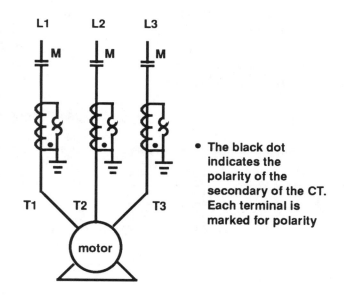

• The black dot indicates the polarity of the secondary of the CT. Each terminal is marked for polarity

51

MAGNETIC MOTOR STARTER

Most applications require the motor controller to be capable of operation from remote locations, or to provide **automatic** operation in response to signals from limit switches, pressure switches, float switches, thermostats, etc. Manual starters cannot provide this type of control, and therefore **magnetic** motor starters are used.

The operating principle which distinguishes a **magnetic** from a **manual** starter is the use of an electromagnetic coil as used in the relay .

The basic difference between a magnetic motor starter and a relay or contactor is the motor starter provides thermal overload protection.

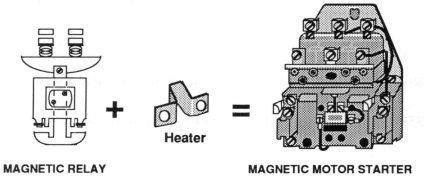

MAGNETIC RELAY   MAGNETIC MOTOR STARTER

With the manual motor starter, the starter must be mounted so that it is easily accessible to the operator. With a magnetic motor starter, the limit switches, pressure switches, etc. can be mounted anywhere on the machine and connected by the control wiring to the coil of the magnetic motor starter.

The Code requires a thermal overload relay to be installed:

Single-phase motor, 2-wire, ungrounded----------------------one in either conductor

Single-phase motor, 2-wire, one conductor grounded-------one in the **ungrounded** conductor

Three-phase motor, 3-wire------------------------------------one in **each** phase

On a schematic drawing, the thermal overload (heater) will be shown by the symbol —ᴄᴄ—.

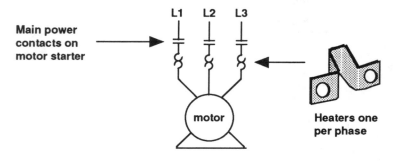

52

As we work our way through the wiring diagrams for motor control circuits, you'll find some circuits have a higher voltage (power) to the motor and a lower voltage for the control signals. A 480 volt motor with 120 volt control is very common. The power wiring to the motor will be shown with a heavier bold line than the control wiring.

Also, remember all diagrams will show the circuit as it appears, OFF or de-energized. The contacts shown as normally open will close when the coil they are physically operated by is energized. Any normally closed contact will open when its coil is energized. The exception to this will be the overload interlock contact. It is not controlled by the coil, but rather by the tripping action of the thermal overload relay. Time delay contacts also do not always open and close as the coil is energized. Please keep these points in mind as you read the diagrams.

WIRING			
NOT CONNECTED	CONNECTED	CONTROL	POWER

In order to properly read a schematic diagram of a magnetic motor starter, I feel you should understand how a motor starter is constructed and the function of the components.

A three-phase motor starter has 3 power contacts that switch the current to the motor. The magnetic starter contains a coil that when energized, closes the power contacts. The starter contains 3 thermal overloads, one per phase. Also the magnetic starter contains one normally open control contact which is used as a holding circuit for the coil.

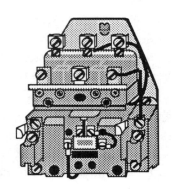

Smaller fractional horsepower motors used a manual starter in which the thermal overloads opened the power to the motor. This is not the case with the magnetic motor starter which normally is used to carry much larger currents. The current is too large for the overload to interrupt the line. A magnetic starter is used with the power contacts interrupting the line. The thermal overloads actually trip a normally closed control interlock that is wired in series with the coil. When an overload occurs the interlock is opened which de-energizes the coil which opens the power contacts to the motor.

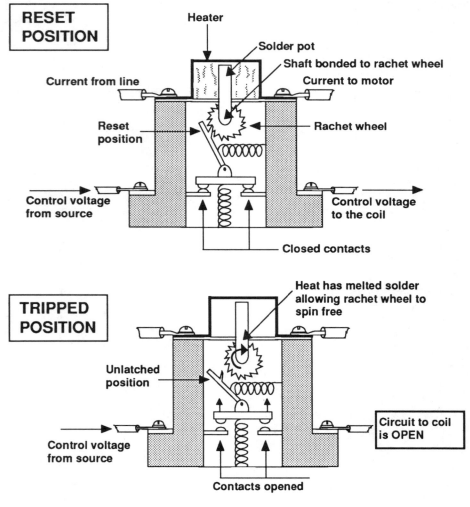

54

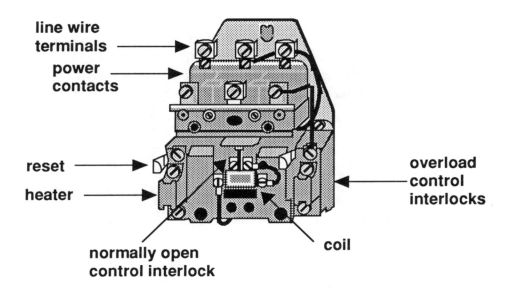

line wire terminals

power contacts

reset

heater

overload control interlocks

normally open control interlock

coil

Shown below is a main wiring diagram of a three-phase magnetic motor starter with 3 thermal overloads. The starter is controlled by a start-stop push button control circuit using the holding circuit. The 3 overload interlocks ⌇ are connected in series with the coil. The 3 thermal overloads —ᴈᴈ— are connected in series with the motor. The control wires are shown in a fine line, the power wires in a heavier line.

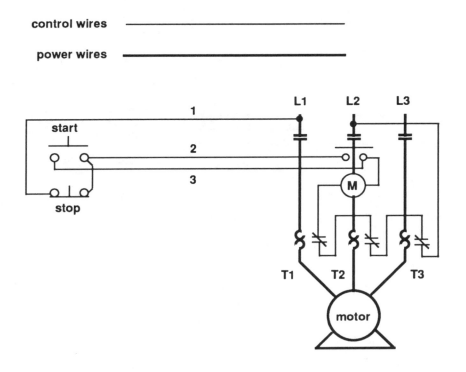

control wires

power wires

The schematic drawing, sometimes called the elementary, shows the same magnetic motor starter, only in an easier diagram for a troubleshooter to follow. The schematic diagram does not show the physical location of the motor starter components, but rather the relationship to each other.

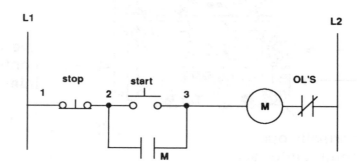

Although motors generally run in only one direction, there are applications when a motor may be required to run in a reverse direction. A three phase motor can be reversed by reversing any two wires. Although it will work, it is not standard to reverse **L2** with L1 or L3. A diagram for a motor starter will show reversing L1 and L3.

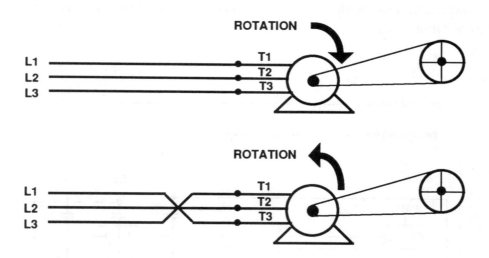

A basic 4-way switch can reverse a three phase motor. A 4-way switch has a limited current rating and would have restricted applications in motor controls.

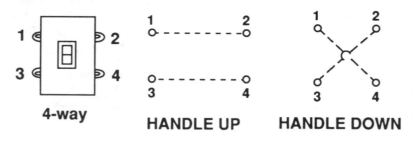

56

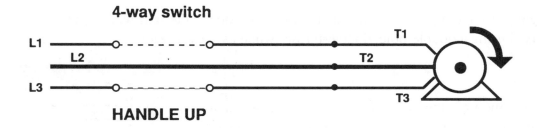

4-way switch

L1 —— L2 —— L3 ——

HANDLE UP

T1 T2 T3

4-way switch

L1 —— L2 —— L3 ——

HANDLE DOWN

T1 T2 T3

Shown below are two sets of 3 power contacts on a reversing motor starter. The control circuit with coils is not shown, only the power in this diagram. When contacts X-Y-Z close, the motor would run in a forward direction. To reverse the direction of the motor, contacts X-Y-Z would open, contacts A-B-C would close. Note that contact "A" is connected to L1 and L3, contact "C" is connected to L3 and L1, this reverses the motor by changing these two wires.

Contacts X-Y-Z would be controlled by the **FORWARD** coil and contacts A-B-C by the **REVERSE** coil.

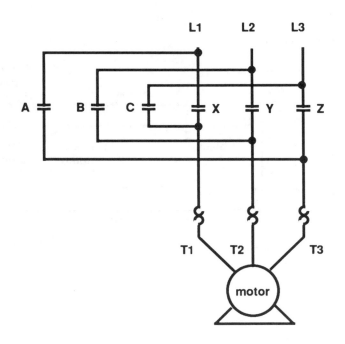

A single phase (split phase) motor that requires the leads of the start winding to be reversed, can be reversed using a double-pole, double-throw switch as shown below.

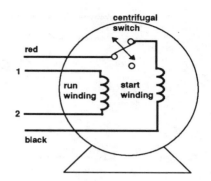

The start winding is the "red" and "black" wires. One motor direction would have "red" connected to **1** and "black" connected to **2.** To reverse the rotation, the start windings are reversed by connecting "red" to **2** and "black" to **1.**

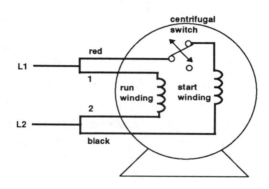

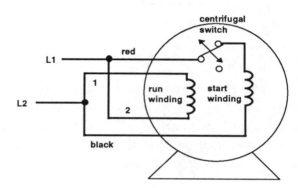

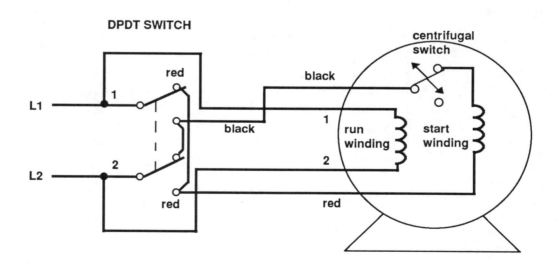

Shown below is a main wiring diagram for a forward-reverse magnetic motor starter. The "F" coil is energized by pushing the forward button which sends a signal through wire **3** through the normally closed interlock on the reverse, and wire **6** to the forward coil. When the forward coil energizes, power contacts F-F-F close, sending voltage to the motor, also the forward coil has a holding circuit through the **6** wire and **3** wire on the normally closed contactor of reverse through the normally open contact on forward, as it is now closed, sending the control signal through wire **2** through the forward button normally closed contact and through the normally closed contact of the stop button to L1. To reverse the motor, the "stop" button must be pressed, which will de-energize the forward coil. When the reverse button is pushed, a signal through the **5** wire through the normally closed contact on forward, through the **7** wire to the reverse coil. When the reverse coil is energized, power contacts R-R-R close, sending voltage to the motor with L1 and L3 being reversed. Also the reverse coil has a holding circuit through wire **7** to wire **5** through the normally closed contacts on the forward, through the normally open contact on reverse which is now closed, through wire **4** through the normally closed contact on the forward button through the normally closed contact on the stop button to L1.

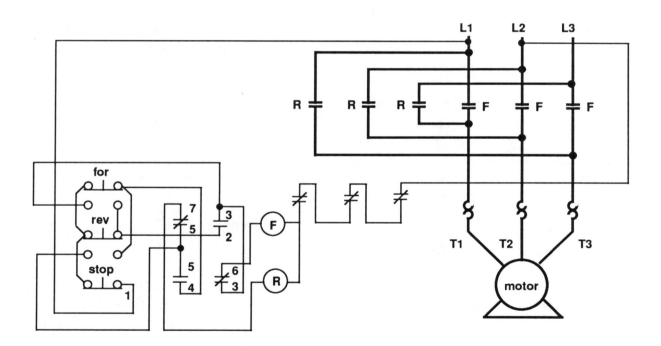

A schematic diagram of a forward-reverse motor starter as shown below is much easier to follow.

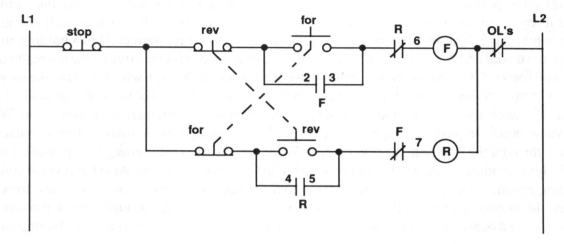

By pressing the "for" button a signal is sent through the normally closed contact of reverse, through the **6** wire to energize the forward coil. The holding circuit is through the **6** wire, through the normally closed reverse, through the **3** wire, through the normally open **F** contact which is now closed since the forward coil is energized, through the **2** wire, through the normally closed "rev" button, through the normally closed "stop" button to L1.

To reverse the motor, press the "stop" button which will de-energize the forward coil. Press the "rev" button and a signal is sent through the normally closed contact of forward, through the **7** wire to energize the reverse coil. The holding circuit is through the **7** wire, through the normally closed forward, through the **5** wire, through the normally open **R** contact which is now closed since the reverse coil is energized, through the **4** wire, through the normally closed "for" button, through the normally closed "stop" button to L1.

A **mechanical** interlock between the "forward" starter and the "reverse" starter prevents both starters from closing at the same time.

When the "forward" starter is energized and closed, the mechanical interlock prevents the closing of the "reverse" contacts. Same is true when the "reverse" starter is energized, the "forward" contacts cannot close.

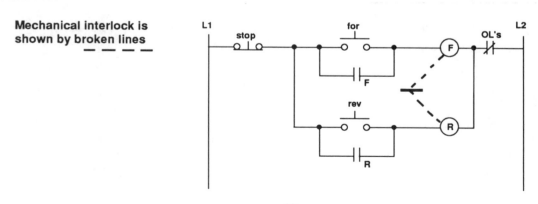

Mechanical interlock is shown by broken lines
— — — —

60

Electrical interlocks are simply normally closed contacts from one starter wired in series with the control circuit to the other starter.

When the "for" button is pushed and **F** coil energizes, the normally closed contacts of **F** are wired in series with the **R** coil and prevent **R** coil from energizing, even if the "rev" button is pushed.

The **R** coil can only be energized if the "stop" button is pushed first, which will de-energize **F** coil and allow the normally closed contacts in the reverse circuit to close. With the normally closed **F** contacts now closed, the "rev" button can be pushed, and **R** coil will energize. When **R** coil energizes, the **R** normally closed contacts open in the forward control circuit and prevent **F** coil from energizing if the "for" button is pushed. This type of interlock is referred to as an **electrical** interlock, since the prevention of energizing both starters at the same time is achieved electrically and not mechanically.

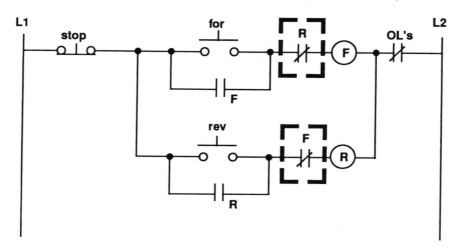

Shown below is a diagram that has pushbutton interlocking, another way of protecting a reversing circuit from damage that could be caused by a line to line short. **Double pole** circuit pushbuttons are used and wired into the circuit so that when the "for" button is pushed, the normally closed contacts of the "for" button open and break the reverse circuit before the normally open contacts close and energize the **F** coil. The "rev" button is wired in the same manner. By wiring the buttons so they open one circuit before closing another, the machine operator **can go from forward to reverse without pushing the stop button first**. Actually, the buttons act first as stop buttons, then start buttons. A broken line drawn between two pushbuttons indicates they are tied together mechanically.

The best protection is still the **mechanical interlock**. It should be used whenever possible.

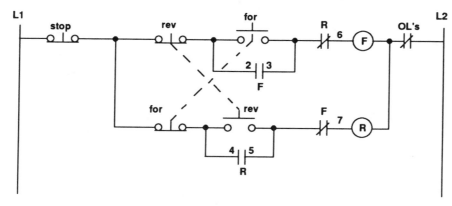

The circuit shown below has limit switches added in the reversing control. An overhead door uses this type of circuit which stops the motor when it has reached a predetermined amount of travel.

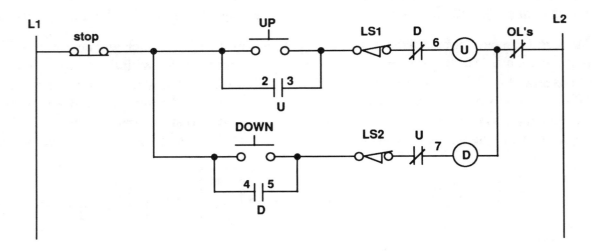

When the "UP" button is pushed, the U coil energizes, the door starts up. The motor will continue to run until LS1 is opened, which will de-energize the U coil. When the "DOWN" button is pushed, the door will start down. The motor will continue to run until LS2 is opened, which de-energizes the D coil. The door can be stopped while traveling in either direction by pushing the "STOP" button. A door safety switch can be added and wired in series with LS2 in the down portion of the circuit to stop the door if a vehicle or other obstruction is in the doorway path as the door is closing.

TWO-SPEED MOTOR STARTING

Shown below is a full-voltage multi-speed diagram. A typical multi-speed starter consists of a group of contactor assemblies in a single enclosure, each contactor operating the motor at one speed. When the "slow" button is pressed, the slow-speed winding is connected to the line and holding contacts across the button, and will hold the circuit closed after the release of the button. To change to fast speed, the button "fast" is pressed, breaking the circuit to the slow-speed contactor and closing the circuit to the fast-speed contactor. The motor then runs at fast speed.

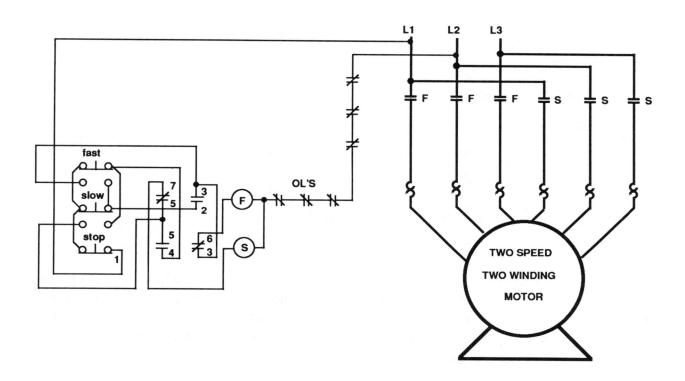

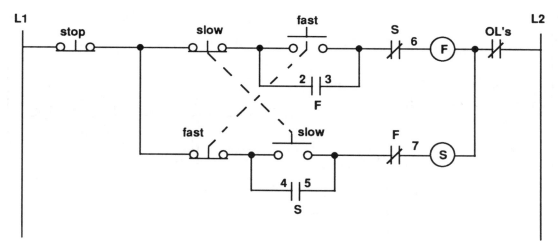

JOG-RUN CIRCUIT

Shown below is a START-STOP-JOG circuit. Start-stop pushbuttons are used with a selector switch. The circuit to normally open holding contact is broken when the selector switch is in the "JOG" position. The "START" button is used to "JOG" or "RUN" the motor, depending on the position of the selector switch.

When the "start" button is pushed, the **3** wire sends a signal energizing the "M" coil which closes the normally open "M" contact, this is a holding circuit through the "run" position of the selector switch, through the normally closed contact of the "stop" button to L1.

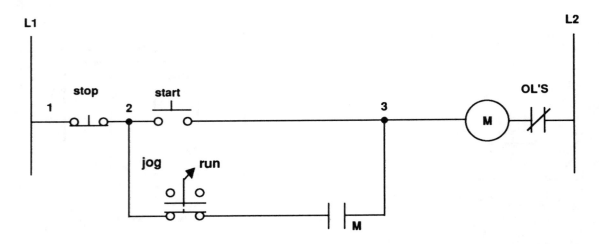

The circuit shown below shows the selector switch turned to the "jog" position. This opens the contact in the "holding circuit". Now the "start" button becomes a "jog" or inch button, the motor will run as long as the "start" button is held closed. When releasing the "start" button the motor will stop as the holding circuit has been broken through the "jog" position of the selector switch.

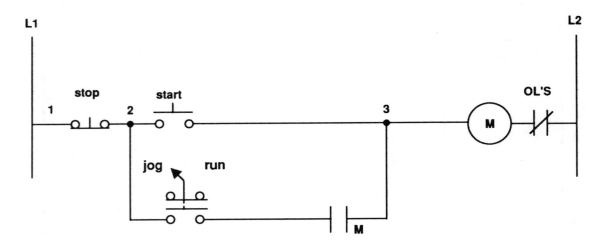

Shown below is the main wiring diagram of the JOG circuit.

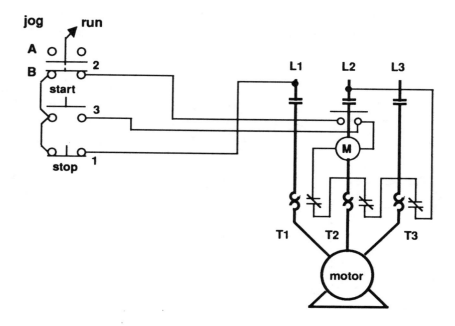

Shown below is the manufacturer's chart showing the position of the selector switch contacts. When the switch is turned to the "left" contact **A** closes. When the switch is turned to the "right" contact **B** closes.

Selector Switch Contacts	Position	
	Left	Right
A	X	
B		X

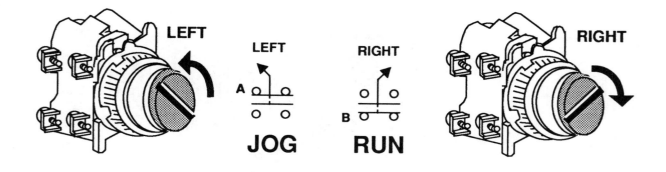

TIME DELAY STARTING

In some cases, the distribution system does not have the capacity to start several large motors at the same time. A time delay can be provided between the starting of motors as shown below. Both motors operate from the same stop-start push buttons.

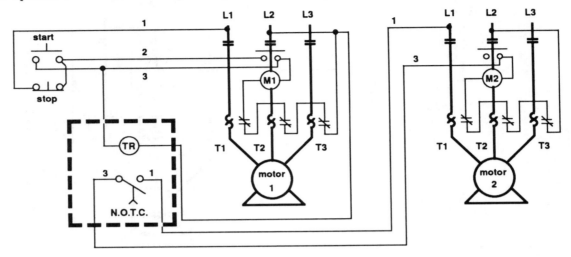

When the "start" button is pushed a signal is sent to the **M1** coil and the **TR** coil through wire **3**. With the **TR** coil energized, the timing action starts. The normally open **TR** contact remains **open** during this timing period. When the pre-set time delay runs out the normally open **TR** contact will **close**. When the contact closes it sends a signal to **M2** coil through the **3** wire which energizes **M2** coil closing the power contacts and starting motor 2.

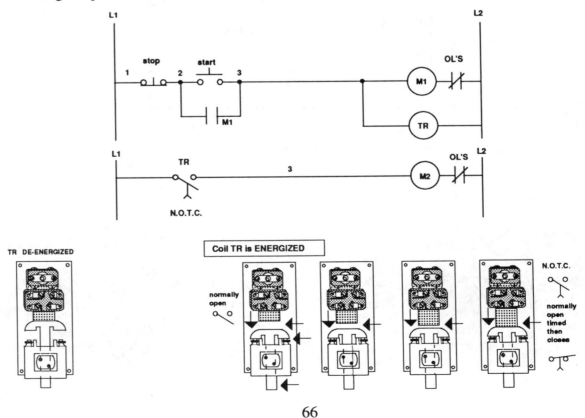

66

RESISTOR STARTING

Full voltage starting of motors can cause problems in some cases. In cases where the supply system does not have the capacity to handle the currents being drawn on start up, line voltage disturbances can be severe.

The way to solve this problem is to use reduced-voltage starting of the motor. The easist way to start a motor at reduced voltage is to connect a **resistor** in series in each motor conductor. The starting current is thereby reduced, and the resistors can be removed from the circuit when the motor has reached a certain speed. The motor then runs at full line voltage.

A typical unit contains one contactor which connects the motor to three line conductors through three resistors to start. After a definite time delay, when the motor has reached speed, another contactor closes and shunts around the resistors.

When the "start" button is pushed, the **M** coil and **TR** coil are energized. The **M** power contacts are closed, completing the power circuit to the motor through a resistor in each phase, which allows the motor to start under a lower voltage. At the same time the time delay is in operation, when it times out the normally open contact closes, which energizes **CR** coil and closes **CR** power contacts, allowing "FULL" voltage to the motor through the path of least resistance.

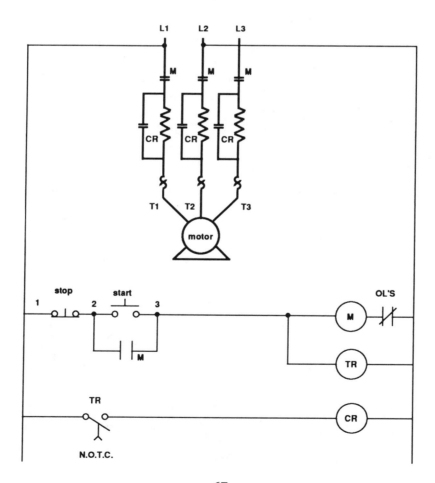

AUTOTRANSFORMER STARTING

The most widely used type of reduce-voltage starting for three-phase squirrel-cage motors is the autotransformer type, offering current limiting and higher starting torque per amp than other reduced-voltage starting, without the energy loss of resistor type starting.

An autotransformer consists of three autotransformer coils, one in each motor conductor. Each transformer coil is generally tapped at one or more points along its winding The taps are to provide different values or reduced voltage for starting such as 80%, 65%, and 50% of the full line voltage to be applied to the motor.

The switching operations are made by magnetic contactors in combination with a timing device. The timing device initiates the transfer from reduce voltage starting to full voltage in the run position.

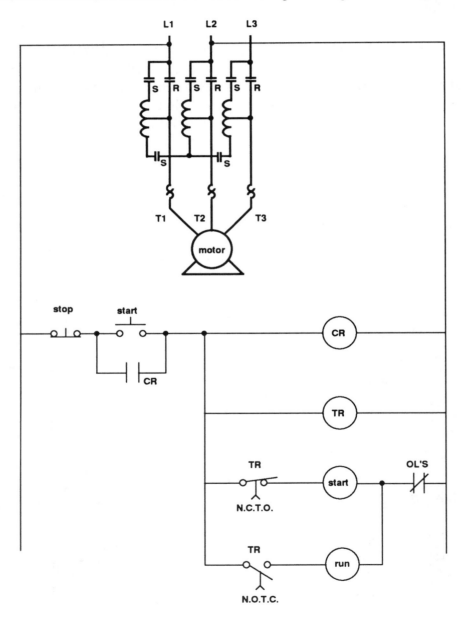

Shown below is a step by step sequence of the autotransformer type reduced-voltage starting.

First step, close the line switch energizing L1, L2, and L3.

L1 becomes energized and follows a path to one side of the start button through the normally closed interlocks on the stop button.

L2 (which also becomes energized when the line switch is closed) follows a path to the "CR" coil and "TR" coil and through the normally closed overload protection interlocks (OL'S) to make one side of "start" coil hot, and also the "run" coil.

When pushing the start button you complete L1 circuit to "CR" coil and "TR" coil which will energize and start the time delay cycle and CR normally open contact closes providing a holding circuit. When pushing the start button the "start" coil is also energized at the same time through the normally closed-timed to open contacts.

At this point with the "start" energized, the normally open "S" contacts on L1-L2-L3 motor circuit and the two normally open "S" contacts in the motor circuit will close allowing voltage from L1-L2-L3 to flow through the "S" contacts through the autotransformer winding coils and through the overloads (heaters) to the motor windings causing the motor to start.

When the motor circuit reaches the pre-set time, the timer times out, "N.C.T.O." interlock will open causing "start" coil to de-energize. At this same moment "N.O.T.C." interlock will close energizing "run" coil, closing the normally open "R" contacts on L1-L2-L3 in the motor circuit. When "R" contacts close they will by-pass the autotransformer windings and follow a path through the overloads (heaters) to the motor windings, putting the motor in a **full running** position.

Automatic autotransformer reduced-voltage starters:

"S" normally open power contacts: Autotransformer motor starters have a period between the start and run positions when the motor is temporarily disconnected from the power lines. The open period starts when the start contactor is de-energized, and ends when the run starter is energized. This de-energized period, called the "open circuit transition", can be objectionable. A sharp spike of current may be drawn when the motor is reconnected across the line in the run position. To overcome this inrush of current caused by the "open circuit transition" from reduced voltage to across-the-line running, a closed circuit transition is very often used.

If the run contactor is closed before the start contactor is opened, high currents that might damage the windings and contacts will flow in the transformer. Since this method cannot be satisfactorily used, some answer to the problem must be found by using some additional equipment.

The most well known solution is called the **"Korndorfer Method"**. This approach uses a third contactor to open the common connection to the autotransformer before the run contactor is energized. The third contactor may "short out" a reactor without damage to it. Thus, the run contactor is energized without having to de-energize the start contactor, resulting in a closed circuit transition.

REACTOR STARTING

Inductive reactance can be used instead of resistance or autotransformer type reduced-voltage starting. Reactors are used in series with the motor conductors instead of resistors. The application is essentially the same as that of resistors.

When using resistors or reactors for reduced-voltage starting, the starting current is directly proportional to the voltage taps. This differs from the use of autotransformer starting, in which the percent of current is lower than the percent of the voltage tap. Autotransformers provide better **current limiting** on the starting in-rush currents.

For the same number of steps as resistance starting, reactor starting can provide the smoothest method of reduced-voltage starting. Reactor starting has a higher starting efficiency, but reactor starting reduces the already low power factor of the starting circuit by increasing the phase angle.

Reactor starting provides heavy-duty use for induction motors, but this method of starting is not generally used except in case of high current or high voltage where size and extreme heating of resistors could be a problem.

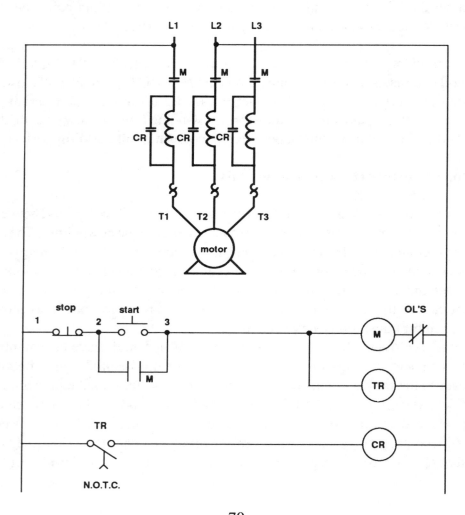

ACCIDENTAL STARTING

Any magnetic motor controller used on a three-phase, 3-wire **ungrounded** system always presents the possibility of accidental starting of the motor.

Shown below is an example, an undetected ground fault exists on L1, a **second** ground fault occurs in the remote control circuit. The motor can accidentally start through this new path of L1 through ground to the coil.

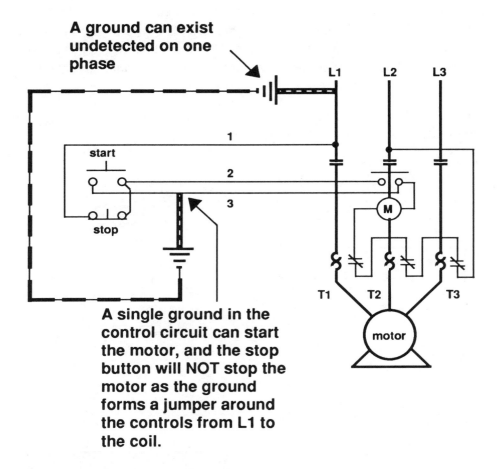

A control transformer can prevent this situation as it will isolate the power circuit (L1) from the remote control circuit.

Remember, to energize a coil it takes about **85%** of the rated coil voltage, but it takes only about **50%** of the rated value for the coil to hold the contacts closed.

Even partial grounds and shorts on control device contacts can produce paths for sufficient current flow to cause shorting of stop button, short-out overload relays, eliminate overcurrent protection, etc.

71

The Code states that the proper use of suitable ground detectors on **ungrounded** systems can provide additional protection.

Ground detectors are often used with the three-phase, three-wire **ungrounded** system.

The sketch below on the left shows a ground detector system that consists of three light bulbs.

The three-phase ground detector system consists of a lamp connected to each phase and connected to ground. All three lamps light **dimly** when there are no grounds. If any phase becomes grounded, the lamp connected to that phase dims even more or goes out completely while the other two lamps will become **brighter**. The sketch below on the right shows "A" phase to ground. The light for "A" phase now goes out and the bulbs for "B" phase and "C" phase glow brighter as the voltage takes the path of least resistance. The grounded metal would have less resistance than the bulb.

The lamps should be the same wattage and voltage. The lamps should be placed close together so you can detect the slightest difference in brightness.

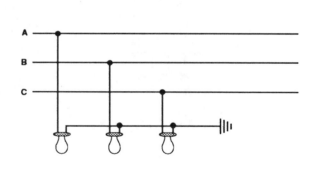
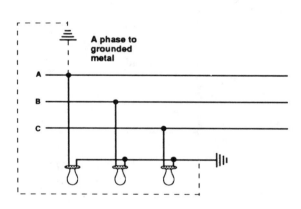

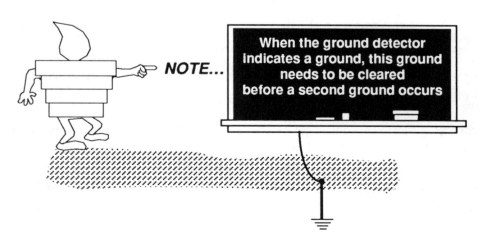

NOTE... When the ground detector indicates a ground, this ground needs to be cleared before a second ground occurs

It's very common to have a step down transformer in the motor control circuit to provide a control circuit voltage lower than the line voltage for reasons of operator safety. Generally, if the line voltage is 480 volts to the motor, the control voltage is 120 volts.

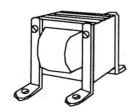

The secondary of the transformer may be operated with one conductor grounded. In some cases this has caused difficulties. For instance, there are cases where a ground fault on the hot wire (ungrounded) of a grounded control circuit can cause a **hazard** to personnel by blowing the fuse or tripping the circuit breaker and shutting down an industrial process in an unexpected way. Example; an overhead conveyor with a magnet that holds a heavy metal piece is being transported to the assembly line. You don't want the fuse to blow and open the circuit to the magnet and drop the metal piece on an assembly line worker below.

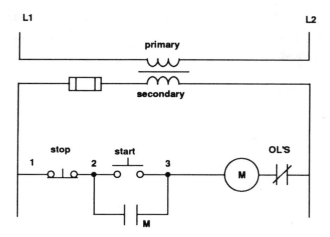

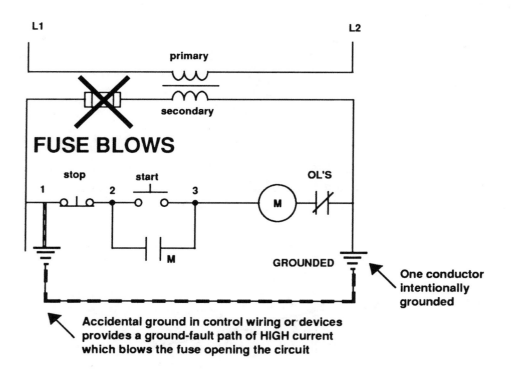

FUSE BLOWS

GROUNDED

One conductor intentionally grounded

Accidental ground in control wiring or devices provides a ground-fault path of HIGH current which blows the fuse opening the circuit

For this reason, the Code in section 250-5b exception 3 permits the control circuit to be **ungrounded**.

73

GROUNDED CONTROL CIRCUIT

The Code permits the low voltage control to be grounded or ungrounded. But, if the low voltage is **grounded** it must be grounded correctly as shown below. If connected wrong, an accidental ground will energize the coil and start the motor as the other side of the coil has voltage. Not only will the motor start automatically, but it cannot be shut off with the "stop" button because the ground path has bypassed the "stop" button by shunting it out of the circuit. This is covered in the Code in section 430-73 which states: Where one side of the motor control circuit is **grounded**, the motor control circuit shall be so arranged that an accidental ground in the remote-control devices **will not start the motor**.

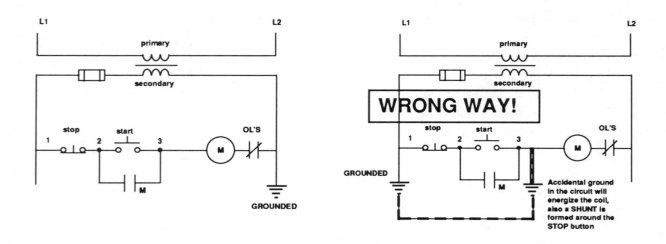

Because many remote-control circuits are long, possible faults have many points at which they can occur. Insulation breakdowns, grounds to raceways, contact shorts due to the accumulation of dirt, oil or moisture are common faults that are responsible for the accidental starting of a motor starter.

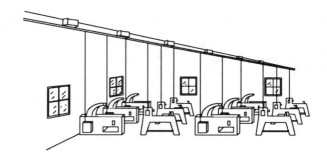

Code section 240-3 exception 3: Power Loss Hazard. Conductor **overload** protection shall not be required where the interruption of the circuit would **create a hazard**, such as in a material handling magnet circuit. Short-circuit protection shall be provided.

Code section 380-2b states that switches shall not disconnect the grounded conductor of a circuit. The exception allows disconnection of the grounded conductor only when **all** conductors of the circuit are disconnected **simultaneously**.

A switch is defined as a device that will make, break, or change the electrical connections of a circuit.

Section 240-22 states: No overcurrent device shall be connected in series with any conductor that is intentionally grounded. An exception states where required in sections 430-36 and 430-37 for motor overload protection. Table 430-37 does **not** show an overload in the grounded conductor. Most schematics show the overload **normally closed interlock** between the coil and L2. But, this would open the grounded conductor when an overload occurs which de-energizes the coil, but wires **1** and **2** would not be **disconnected**. Some schematics will show the overload interlocks on the **other** side of the coil.

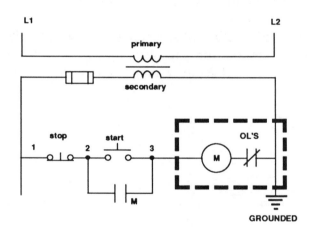

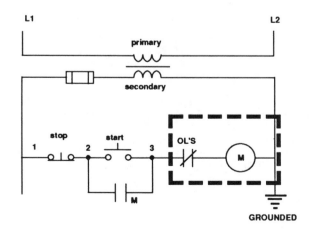

Motors in some cases are required to be protected by more than one type of protection. The most commonly used protections applicable to motors are:

1. Overload protection
2. Undervoltage protection
3. Phase-reversal protection
4. Open-phase protection

In certain motor applications, it is required to install relays which are designed to operate on a certain specified voltage. If the voltage is too low it can cause motor damage. In this application, a **very sensitive undervoltage** relay is required. Under normal voltage conditions the coil is held in and the contacts are closed and the motor runs. With a change (lower) in voltage, it will de-energize the undervoltage coil opening the contacts that are in series with the stop button.

Remember, to energize a coil it takes about 85% of the rated coil voltage, but it takes only about 50% of the rated value for the coil to hold the contacts closed.

Example; a 240 volt coil x 85% = 204 volts. Approximately 204 volts could energize a 240 volt rated coil. It is possible the voltage could drop to 240 volts x 50% = 120 volts before the contacts open. If this did happen, damage could be done to certain electrical equipment.

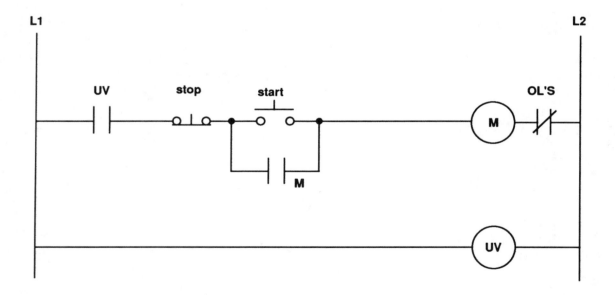

MECHANICAL LATCH

A magnetic motor starter **without** thermal overload protection (heaters) is a magnetic contactor. A variation of the magnetic contactor is the **mechanically held** contactor, in which the coil is momentarily **energized to close** the contacts and then momentarily **energized to open** the contacts.

Often referred to as "latching relays" or "latching contactors". Since the contacts are mechanically held closed after the coil has been de-energized voltage dips or failures will not change its operating position. Latched contactors offer an advantage on power or lighting circuits where conditions of voltage fluctuation exist. There would be no humming noise from the coil armature vibration.

Shown below is a typical control circuit for a mechanical latching relay. When the "ON" button is pressed, the latch coil energizes and opens the normally closed L contacts and closes the U contacts. When L opens, the latch coil de-energizes. From the time the "ON" button is pressed, energizing the latch coil, which opens the normally closed L and de-energizes the latch coil is only a fraction of a second. During the short time the latch coil is energized, it closed the normally open R contacts completing the circuit to the light. R contacts remain closed even though the latch coil de-energizes because of the mechanical latch mechanism. To open the mechanically latched contacts to turn the light off requires pressing the "OFF" button. The U contacts in the unlatch coil circuit are closed, and pressing the "OFF" button energizes the unlatch coil, which in turn closes the normally closed L contacts and opens the U contacts which de-energizes the unlatch coil. For the brief instant that the unlatch coil was energized, it released the mechanically latched R contacts, so it opened, turning off the light.

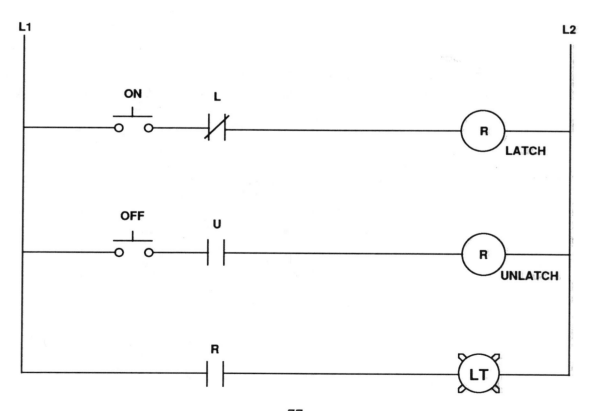

PLUGGING

Plugging is a braking action used to quickly bring a rotating motor to a stop. A plugging switch is a centrifugal switch with a protruding shaft. Inside the switch housing, when the elements are rotated due to rotation of the motor shaft, a centrifugal force is produced which closes a set of contacts for the particular direction of rotation. When the "stop" button is pressed, the forward contactor is opened and a reverse contactor is closed. As the motor slows down due to the application of reverse torque through the reverse contactor, the centrifugal force becomes insufficient to hold the contacts closed in the plugging switch and the reversing contactor opens when the speed slows down. Before actual reversal is accomplished, the reverse (plugging) starter is de-energized, which brings the motor to a rapid stop without reversing direction.

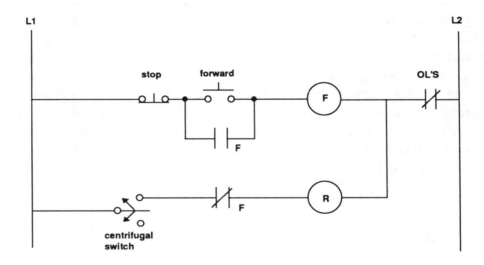

Pressing the "forward" button energizes the **F** starter coil and the motor runs. The forward rotation of the shaft causes the centrifugal switch to close. The normally closed **F** contact is open as the **F** coil is energized.

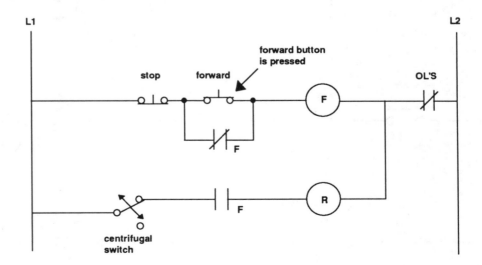

78

When the "stop" button is pressed and the **F** coil is de-energized, the **F** normally closed contacts close which energizes the **R** coil through the closed contact on the centrifugal switch. This reverses the motor as the reverse contactor is energized. As the motor speed slows down, the centrifugal switch will open, de-energizing the **R** contactor coil before the motor actually reverses in direction.

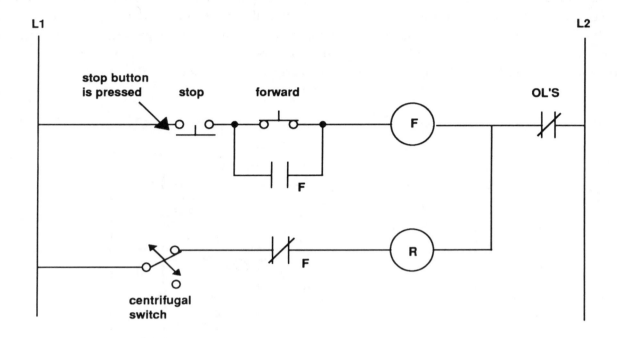

SPEED SWITCH

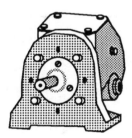

SHUNTING OF OVERLOADS

The Code allows shunting of the overloads during starting in certain cases. The "shunt button" has L1 potential to it all the time through the stop button. When the "start" and "shunt" buttons are pressed the S coil is energized and the three S power contacts close which will bypass the heaters, and the motor will start. As the motor builds up speed the operator will release the "shunt" button and the S power contacts will open. Motor current now flows through the heaters to the motor.

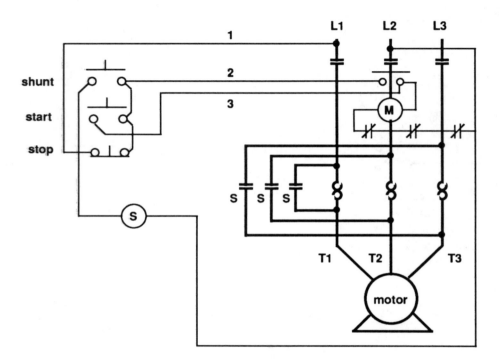

PRESSURE SWITCH CONTROL

Shown below is a magnetic motor starter controlled by a pressure switch with a "high pressure" cut-out or "safety" switch. The circuit also has a manual control selector switch.

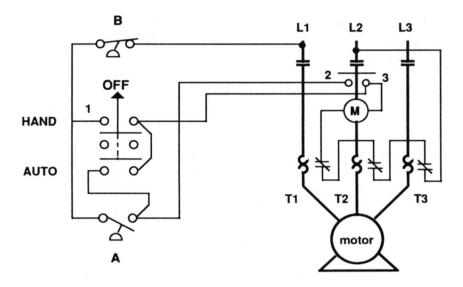

The selector switch makes it possible to operate the magnetic starter manually for testing or in case of failure with the automatic control. The high pressure cut-out switch **"B"** is inserted in L1 leading to the "hand" terminal of the selector switch. The low pressure switch **"A"** is connected with the "auto" terminal of the selector switch.

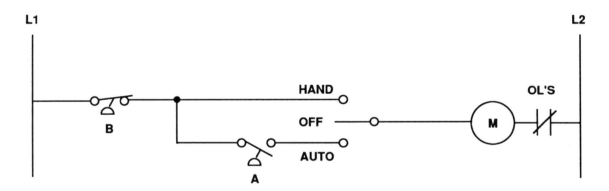

Shown below is a float switch intended for tank operation. When the water reaches "low" level the float switch closes and starts the pump. The pumping action will continue until the water reaches the "high" level.

For sump pumping remove wire"A" and connect as per the dotted line. At "low" level the float switch operates and stops the pumping action. Sump pumping action will not commence until the water reaches the "high" level.

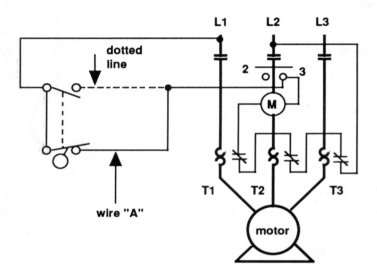

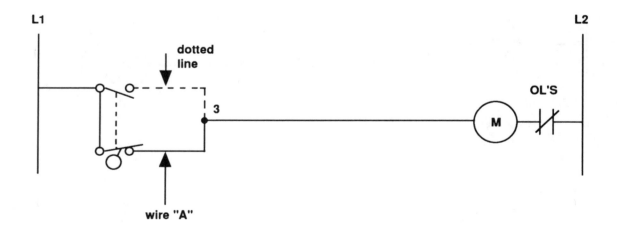

PILOT LIGHT CIRCUIT

Pilot lights are used in control circuits to indicate when the motor is running as shown below. The pilot light can be wired in parallel with the **M** coil, or it may be wired with an auxiliary **M** contact.

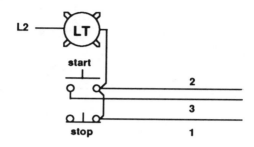

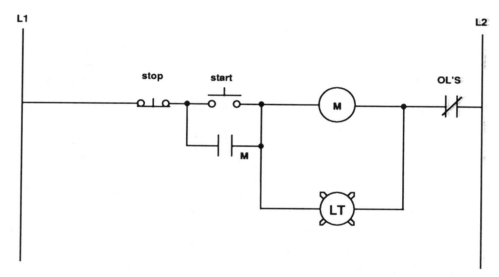

When the pilot light is located out of sight from the motor, there may be doubt as to whether the motor is actually not running or the pilot light bulb is burned out. To eliminate any doubt, a push-to-test pilot light allows the operator to push the button to test the bulb.

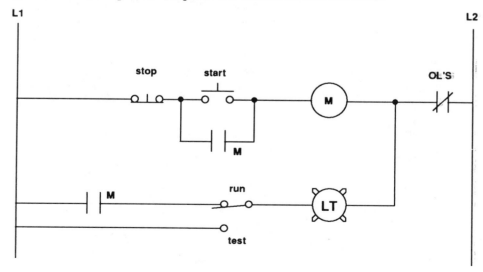

EXAMS

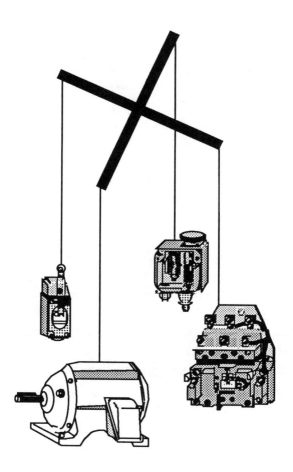

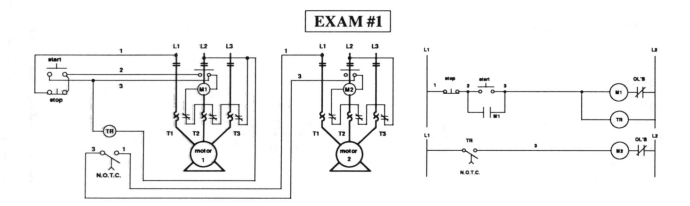

EXAM #1

1. Additional stop stations could be added in _____.

(a) **parallel with the existing stop button**   (b) **series with the existing stop button**
(c) **parallel with the existing start button**   (d) **only for motor #2**

2. The pilot light is on only when _____.

(a) **the motors are running**
(b) **the timer times out and until the stop button is opened**
(c) **the start button is closed and stays on until the stop button is opened**
(d) **there is no pilot light**

3. Which of the following is a true statement concerning the control circuit?

(a) **The purpose of the timing relay is to prevent the second motor from starting before the first
     motor comes up to speed.**
(b) **The purpose of the timing relay is to remove the second motor after a period of time and
     allow the first motor to remain on the line.**
(c) **The purpose of the timing relay is to prevent the second motor from running while the first
     motor is on the line.**
(d) **The O.L. heaters are in series with both M1 and M2.**

4. Which of the following is the correct sequence of operation?

(a) **The start button is pushed, M1 is energized, N.O.T.C. opens and M2 is energized.**
(b) **The start button is pushed, M1 and TR are energized, N.O.T.C. closes and M2 is energized.**
(c) **The start button is pushed, M1 is energized, M closes and the second motor starts.**
(d) **The start button is pushed, TR is energized, N.O.T.C. closes and M1 and M2 are energized
     simultaneously.**

85

EXAM #2

•Fill in the blank with the correct letter from choices below for the symbol

1. _____ 2. _____ 3. _____ 4. _____ 5. _____ 6. _____

7. _____ 8. _____ 9. _____ 10. _____ 11. _____ 12. _____

13. _____ 14. _____ 15. _____ 16. _____ 17. _____ 18. _____

19. _____ 20. _____

•Choose a letter ( ) and fill in the blank above:

(A) CB with thermal O.L.	**(K)** SPDT double break
(B) normally closed contact	**(L)** normally open contact
(C) liquid level switch N.C.	**(M)** temperature actuated switch N.C.
(D) temperature actuated switch N.O.	**(N)** thermal O.L.
(E) foot switch N.C.	**(O)** selector switch-two position
(F) start button N.O.	**(P)** foot switch N.O.
(G) Timed contact N.O.T.C.	**(Q)** limit switch N.C.
(H) stop button N.C.	**(R)** autotransformer winding
(I) disconnect	**(S)** liquid level switch N.O.
(J) limit switch N.O.	**(T)** mushroom head push button switch

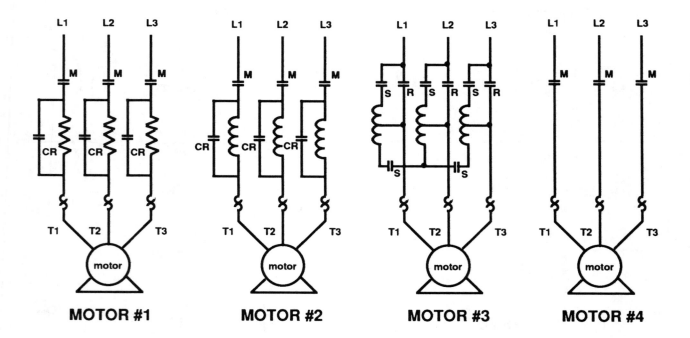

MOTOR #1   MOTOR #2   MOTOR #3   MOTOR #4

1. Motor #1 is a _____ type start.

(a) full voltage   (b) autotransformer   (c) resistor   (d) reactor

2. Motor #2 is a _____ type start.

(a) full voltage   (b) autotransformer   (c) resistor   (d) reactor

3. Motor #3 is a _____ type start.

(a) full voltage   (b) autotransformer   (c) resistor   (d) reactor

4. Motor #4 is a _____ type start.

(a) full voltage   (b) autotransformer   (c) resistor   (d) reactor

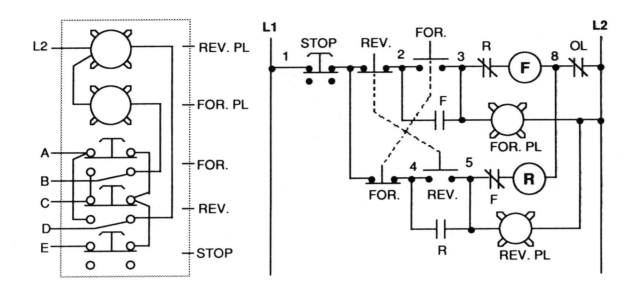

1. Conductor "A" on the push button station is conductor number _____ shown in the control circuit schematic.

(a) 1 (b) 2 (c) 3 (d) 4 (e) 5

2. Conductor "B" on the push button station is conductor number _____ shown in the control circuit schematic.

(a) 1 (b) 2 (c) 3 (d) 4 (e) 5

3. Conductor "C" on the push button station is conductor number _____ shown in the control circuit schematic.

(a) 1 (b) 2 (c) 3 (d) 4 (e) 5

4. Conductor "D" on the push button station is conductor number _____ shown in the control circuit schematic.

(a) 1 (b) 2 (c) 3 (d) 4 (e) 5

5. Conductor "E" on the push button station is conductor number _____ shown in the control circuit schematic.

(a) 1 (b) 2 (c) 3 (d) 4 (e) 5

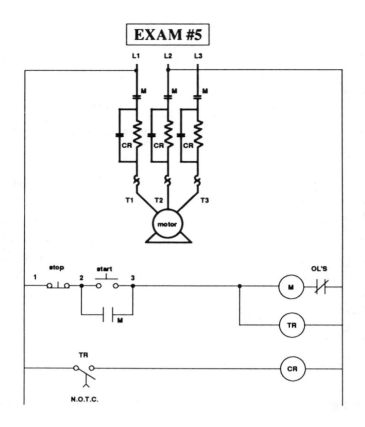

EXAM #5

1. This is a _____ type starter.
(a) **full voltage**   (b) **autotransformer**   (c) **reactor**   (d) **resistor**

2. The resistors are:
(a) **in series with the heaters**   (b) **in parallel with the M contacts**
(c) **in series with the M contacts**   (d) **in parallel with the CR contacts**

3. When the motor is at full speed:
(a) **all normally open CR contacts are closed**
(b) **all normally open M contacts are open**
(c) **OL contacts are open**
(d) **all normally open CR contacts are open**

4. Which is true?
(a) **CR contacts close before M contacts close**
(b) **⊣⊢M opens when ⓉⓇ is energized**
(c) **when ⒸⓇ is energized the motor will go to full run position**
(d) **when ⊣⊢M closes ⒸⓇ is energized**

5. To add another "START" button, you would connect it in:
(a) **series**   (b) **series-parallel**   (c) **parallel**   (d) **L3**

89

1. Which of the following double-pole double-throw switches is properly connected as a reversing switch?

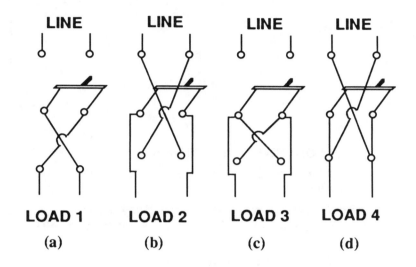

2. Which of the following is the correct wiring to a light controlled by two 3-way switches?

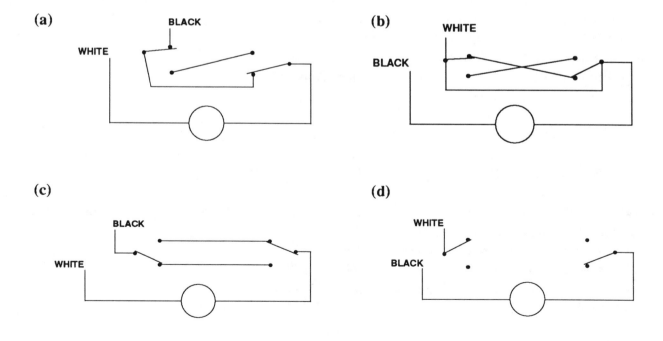

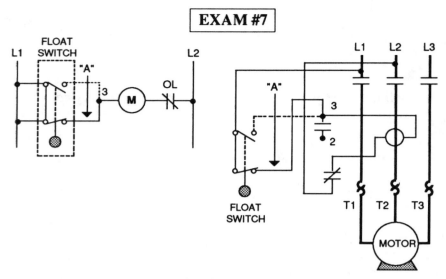

FLOAT SWITCH CONTROLS STARTER

The diagram shows a float switch intended for tank operation. When the water reaches "low" level the float switch closes. Pumping action will continue until the water reaches the "high" level.

For sump pumping remove wire "A" and connect as per the dotted line. At "low" level the float switch operates and stops the pumping action. Sump pumping action will not commence until the water reaches the "high" level.

FLOAT SWITCH SHOWN IN FUEL TANK

1. This is a _____ type starter.
(a) **full voltage**   (b) **resistor**   (c) **reversible**   (d) **reactor**

2. When used for sump pump, if conductor identified as "A" were not installed as per instructions, this control circuit would not function properly because _____.
(a) **the H.C. (pts 2 & 3) have been bypassed**
(b) **the motor would reverse rotation**
(c) **pump would only function when container is empty**
(d) **overloads are bypassed**

3. A remote momentary stop station should be added to _____.
   I. L1   II. L2   III. L3
(a) **I only**   (b) **I and II only**   (c) **I and III only**   (d) **none**

4. Which of the following devices could be wired into the control circuit to provide manual and automatic control regardless of the fluid level?
(a) **An auxiliary contact holding circuit.**
(b) **A three position selector switch.**
(c) **A momentary contact "run" pushbutton.**
(d) **None of these.**

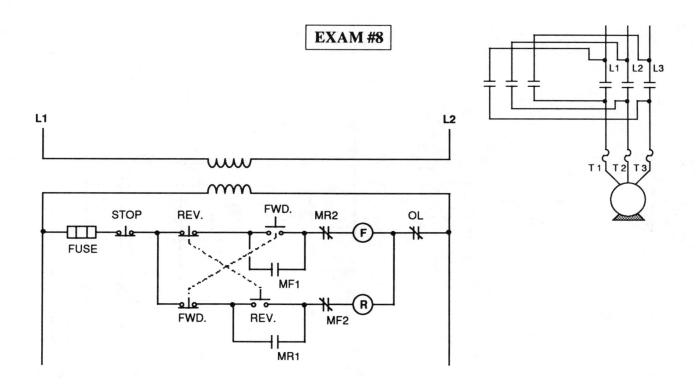

1. To reverse the motor:
    (a) **L1 & L2 are interchanged**   (b) **L2 & L3 are interchanged**
    (c) **L1 & L3 are interchanged**   (d) **the field is reversed**

2. To reverse the motor:
    (a) **The stop button is depressed before the reverse button**
    (b) **The reverse button should be depressed with the motor running forward**
    (c) **MR2 must be closed**
    (d) **MF2 must be open**

3. To run in the forward direction, which of the following is true?
    (a) **MF1 must close before MR2 opens**
    (b) **MF2 must open before FWD. is released**
    (c) **MF2 must open and MF1 must close before FWD. is released**
    (d) **MF1 must close before FWD. is released**

4. If the motor is running in the reverse direction, which of the following is true?
    (a) **The motor will stop if the FWD. button is depressed but released before MR2 closes and MF1 opens.**
    (b) **The motor will stop if the FWD. button is depressed but released before MF1 and MF2 opens.**
    (c) **The motor will stop if the FWD. button is depressed but released after MF1 and MF2 close.**
    (d) **The motor will stop if the FWD. button is depressed but released after MR1 opens and before MF1 closes.**

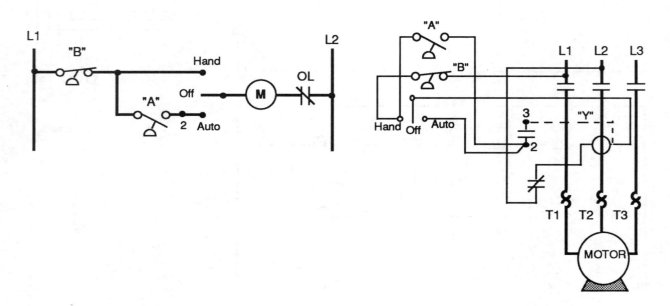

1. This is a _____ type starter.

(a) full voltage   (b) time-delay   (c) resistor   (d) autotransformer

2. The starter is operated by a pressure switch with manual control provided by a selector switch. The circuit also has a high pressure switch. The low pressure switch is shown connected _____.

(a) between L1 and "Hand" switch   **(b) between "Hand" switch and terminal 2**
(c) between "auto" and terminal 2   **(d) between "Hand" and "Off"**

3. The "high pressure" cut-out switch is inserted in ____.

(a) L3 to the overload   **(b) L1 to the "hand" terminal of the selector switch**
(c) L2 to the overload interlock   **(d) between terminal "2" and the "auto" terminal**

4. The dotted line "Y" from terminal 3 to the coil is ____.

(a) connected when a time-delay is required   **(b) removed for shunt-field starting**
(c) removed for a starter without push buttons   **(d) connected for reactor starting only**

5. In order for the motor to run in the "Auto" position, _____.

(a) only switch "A" has to be closed   **(b) only switch "B" has to be closed**
(c) both switches "A" and "B" must be closed   **(d) neither switch has to be closed**

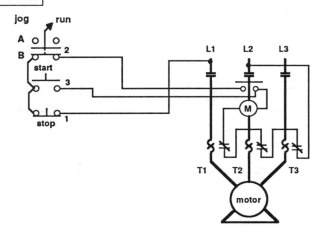

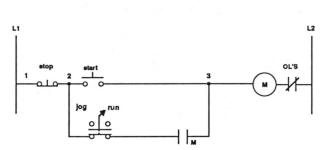

1. This is a _____ type starter.

(a) **reactor**   (b) **autotransformer**   (c) **resistor**   (d) **full voltage**

2. Which of the following is a true statement?
(a) **The Stop station is in parallel with the control circuit.**
(b) **The overload interlocks are in series with ⓜ.**
(c) **The heaters are in series with ⓜ.**
(d) **─┤├─ M is in parallel with ⓜ.**

3. Which of the following is a **false** statement?
(a) **The overload interlocks are in series with L2.**
(b) **The Stop station is in series with ⓜ.**
(c) **The heaters are in parallel with the motor.**
(d) **In the jog mode, ─┤├─ M has been bypassed.**

4. With the control circuit in the jog mode, which is the proper sequence of operation?
(a) **Start is pushed, energizing ─┤├─ M and ⓜ; Stop is pushed, ⓜ releases, jog cycle is complete.**
(b) **Start is pushed, energizing ⓜ, Stop is pushed before ─┤├─ M can lock in.**
(c) **Start is pushed, and ⓜ is energized, ─┤├─ M is bypassed in the jog mode, ⓜ remains energized only when Start is in the closed position.**
(d) **Start is pushed, ─┤├─ M closes and energizes ⓜ, ─┤├─ M then times out and opens the circuit to ⓜ.**

5. With the control circuit in the run mode, which is the proper sequence of operation?
(a) **Start is pushed, ─┤├─ M is bypassed, ⓜ is energized.**
(b) **Start is pushed, energizing ⓜ. ─┤├─ M locks in.**
(c) **Start is pushed, ─┤├─ M locks in, ⓜ is de-energized.**
(d) **Start is pushed, ─┤├─ M locks in, energizing ⓜ.**

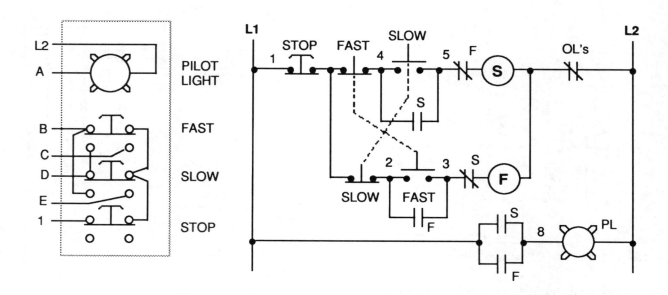

1. "**A**" is actually point _____ on the control diagram.

(a) **L1**   (b) **L2**   (c) **8**   (d) **6**

2. "**D**" is actually point _____ on the control diagram.

(a) **5**   (b) **4**   (c) **3**   (d) **2**

3. "**B**" is actually point _____ on the control diagram.

(a) **4**   (b) **3**   (c) **2**   (d) **L1**

4. "**C**" is actually point _____ on the control diagram.

(a) **4**   (b) **3**   (c) **2**   (d) **L1**

5. "**E**" is actually point _____ on the control diagram.

(a) **4**   (b) **5**   (c) **1**   (d) **2**

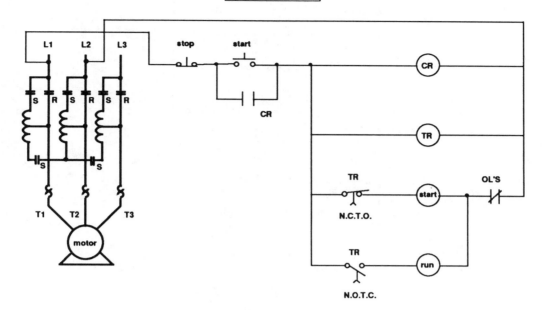

EXAM #12

1. This is a _____ type starter.

(a) **full voltage** (b) **autotransformer** (c) **reactor** (d) **resistor**

2. What is the sequence of the operation?

(a) **N.C.T.O. opens, when N.O.T.C. closes** (b) ⊣⊢**R** closes, then ⊣⊢**S** opens

(c) ⊣⊢**S** closes, then ⊣⊢**CR** closes (d) ⊣⊢**S** closes, then ⊣⊢**CR** opens

3. What is the sequence of operation?

(a) (S) energized, then (CR) (b) (CR) energized, then (TR)

(c) (TR) and (CR) energized simultaneously (d) (TR) energized, then (CR)

4. What is the sequence of operation?

(a) N.O.T.C. closes before N.C.T.O. closes (b) ⊣⊢**R** closes, then ⊣⊢**S** closes

(c) ⊣⊢**R** closes before N.C.T.O. opens (d) ⊣⊢**S** opens at the same time ⊣⊢**R** closes

5. Which of the following is true?

I. When N.C.T.O. opens and N.O.T.C. closes, the **run** coil is energized.

II. When the **R** contacts close, full line voltage is applied to the motor.

III. When the **start** coil is de-energized, the **run** coil is energized.

(a) **I only** (b) **II only** (c) **III only** (d) **I, II and III**

96

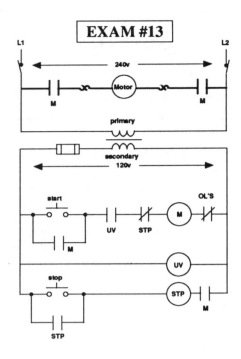

EXAM #13

1. Which of the following statements is true?

(a) The stop button is normally closed
(b) The stop button is normally open
(c) The UV relay is on 240 volts
(d) The start button is sealed by the STP auxiliary contact

2. If the fused disconnect were open the motor would stop because _____.

(a) of undervoltage   **(b) the "M" contacts open**
(c) "M" coil de-energizes   **(d) all of these would happen**

3. Which of the following must occur first before the motor can start?

(a) ⊣├ UV closes   (b) ⫫ STP opens   (c) ⊣├ M closes   (d) ⫫ OL opens

4. When STP coil is energized and sealed in by the auxiliary STP contact, what de-energizes the STP circuit?

(a) ⊣├ UV closes   (b) ⫫ STP opens   (c) ⊣├ M opens   (d) ⫫ STP closes

5. Which of the following is true with the motor running?

(a) ⊣├ UV is open   (b) ⊣├ STP is closed

(c) The UV coil is energized   (d) The ⫫ OL overload is open

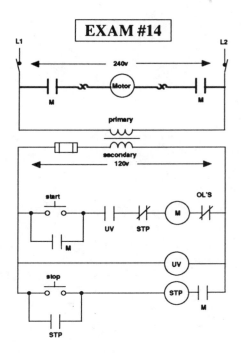

1. When the disconnect is closed, _____.

(a) the motor will start   (b) M coil will energize
(c) STP coil will energize   (d) UV coil will energize

2. STP relay has _____.

(a) a normally open contact   (b) a normally closed contact
(c) a N.C. and N.O. contact   (d) none of these

3. In order to stop the motor under normal conditions, you would _____.

(a) open the disconnect
(b) do nothing, the motor will stop at the end of the control sequence
(c) push the normally open pushbutton around the M contact
(d) push the normally open pushbutton around the STP contact

4. The STP coil will _____.

(a) stay energized momentarily when its PB is closed   (b) cut the UV coil out of the circuit
(c) operate the STP motor after the M coil is energized   (d) none of these

5. Which of the following statements is true?

(a) The stop pushbutton is a N.O. contact which must be closed to stop the motor.
(b) The undervoltage relay is on 240 volts.
(c) The stop pushbutton is a N.C. contact which must be opened to stop the motor.
(d) The start pushbutton is sealed in by the STP auxiliary contact.

98

ANSWERS

EXAM #1

1. **(b)** series with the existing stop button

2. **(d)** there is no pilot light

3. **(a)** The purpose of the timing relay is to prevent the second motor from starting before the first.

4. **(b)** The start button is pushed, M1 and TR are energized, N.O.T.C. closes and M2 is energized.

EXAM #2

1. **J**   2. **F**   3. **E**   4. **K**   5. **Q**   6. **I**   7. **H**   8. **P**   9. **D**   10. **S**

11. **B**   12. **T**   13. **O**   14. **C**   15. **G**   16. **L**   17. **M**   18. **N**   19. **A**   20. **R**

EXAM #3

1. **(c)** resistor start

2. **(d)** reactor start

3. **(b)** autotransformer start

4. **(a)** full voltage start

EXAM #4

1. **(d)** 4

2. **(c)** 3

3. **(b)** 2

4. **(e)** 5

5. **(a)** 1

1. **(d)** resistor

2. **(d)** in parallel with the CR contacts

3. **(a)** all normally open CR contacts are closed

4. **(c)** when CR coil is energized the motor will go to full run position

5. **(c)** parallel

EXAM #6

1. **(b)**   2. **(c)**

EXAM #7

1. **(a)** full voltage

2. **(c)** pump would only function when container is empty

3. **(a)** I only

4. **(b)** A three position selector switch

EXAM #8

1. **(c)** L1 & L3 are interchanged

2. **(a)** The stop button is depressed before the reverse button

3. **(d)** MF1 must close before FWD is released

4. **(d)** The motor will stop if the FWD button is depressed but released after MR1 opens and before MF1 closes

1. **(a)** full voltage

2. **(b)** between "Hand" switch and terminal 2

3. **(b)** L1 to the "Hand" terminal of the selector switch

4. **(c)** removed for a starter without push buttons

5. **(c)** both switches "A" and "B" must be closed

1. **(d)** full voltage

2. **(b)** The overloads are in series with the M coil

3. **(c)** The heaters are in parallel with the motor

4. **(c)** Start is pushed, and M coil is energized, etc.

5. **(b)** Start is pushed, energizing M coil, N.O. "M" locks in

1. **(c)** 8

2. **(d)** 2

3. **(a)** 4

4. **(b)** 3

5. **(b)** 5

1. **(b)** autotransformer

2. **(a)** N.C.T.O. opens, when N.O.T.C. closes

3. **(c)** TR coil and CR coil energized simultaneously

4. **(d)** N.O. "S" opens at the same time N.O. "R" closes

5. **(d)** I, II and III

EXAM #13

1. **(b)** The stop button is normally open

2. **(d)** all of these would happen

3. **(a)** UV closes

4. **(c)** M opens

5. **(c)** The UV coil is energized

EXAM #14

1. **(d)** UV coil will energize

2. **(c)** A N.C. and N.O. contact

3. **(d)** push the normally open pushbutton around the STP contact

4. **(a)** stay energized momentarily when its PB is closed

5. **(a)** The stop pushbutton is a N.O. contact which must be closed to stop the motor

"LEARN TO BE AN ELECTRICIAN"

1996 will mark the start of Tom Henry's NEW venture to actually train a person to become an electrician. With the purchase of 2 1/2 acres and the construction now completed for the Orlando headquarters, excitement is being generated throughout the country with interest in this new venture!

Starting with the toolbelt, safety, theory, practical wiring, Code, etc. Tom Henry will teach the student through his own personally designed **modules and animated videos** from point zero to an electrician that will not only know how, but *why*!

If you're a contractor that has electricians that have never had training, this will be an excellent opportunity to improve the quality and production of your work and have a person knowledgeable of the Code and able to communicate with the inspector.

This will be a correspondance course through the mail with any questions throughout the training course answered by mail, phone or fax. This training course will be offered throughout the *world*. For more information and start dates call today!

The most exciting training program ever developed! Now you'll be able to SEE the electron in orbit and SEE electricity through WATER ANALOGY in ACTION!!

1-800-642-2633

BIG SELLER!

PRE-EXAMS

Order your *complete* Journeyman or Master pre-exam today!

Why take an actual exam, spend all that money, often lose a day of work,when you're not sure if you'll pass?

NOW THE ANXIETY CAN BE REMOVED FROM EXAM TAKING!

Tom Henry has now computer designed actual electrical exams with the percentage of questions from different catagories based just as the exams are. The level of mastery is perfected in each exam. A perfect way to tell if you're ready for the exam.

After completing your *complete* electrical exam you will mail your answer sheet back to Tom Henry and he will personally computer grade it and a grade evaluation sheet will be returned in the same day's mail . You'll know right away your strong and weak areas as the evaluation will point out each in detail so you'll know exactly where you stand with Tom Henry's personal evaluation.

EXAMS WILL DIFFER FROM MONTH TO MONTH

ITEM # 280 - $20.00   JOURNEYMAN COMPLETE 6 HOUR EXAM
50 CLOSED BOOK QUESTIONS   50 OPEN BOOK QUESTIONS
30 CALCULATIONS

ITEM #281 - $20.00   MASTER COMPLETE 6 HOUR EXAM
50 CLOSED BOOK QUESTIONS   70 OPEN BOOK QUESTIONS
30 CALCULATIONS

 Call 1-800-642-2633 Today!

THE BIG SELLER

Now you can have a Code book just like the one Tom Henry uses!

THE "ULTIMATE" 1996 LOOSELEAF CODE BOOK FOR TAKING AN EXAM

It took over 3 1/2 hours but Tom Henry has personally **hi-lited** over *1300* answers to exam questions that have been asked on previous electrical examinations.

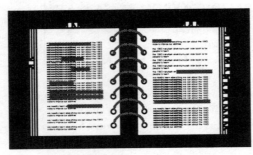

68 TABS ARE INSTALLED FOR YOU!

COLOR
YELLOW = JOURNEYMAN
PINK = MASTER
ORANGE = BOTH Journeyman & Master

DON'T DELAY
ORDER YOURS TODAY!
1-800-642-2633

The Journeyman exam answers are hi-lited with a "yellow" marker, the answers for the Master exams are marked with a "pink" marker. Questions which have been asked on both the Journeyman and Master exams are marked "orange" in color.

The "ULTIMATE" Looseleaf Code book also includes **Tom Henry's** BIG SELLER the "KEY WORD INDEX","REMINDERS FOR THE ELECTRICIAN", 68 "CODE TABS" (**installed for you**) and the popular "FORMULA INSERT

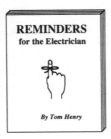

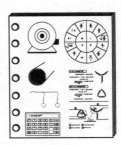